What Others Are Saying About The Fat Burning Diet...

Dear Jay,

A year ago I was a frustrated, unhappy 38 year old woman weighing 145 lb. I was really excited about starting a diet after I saw a video tape of myself on a vacation in Florida. I got on the bald-lady's diet (you know who I mean), I did lose 10 lb. but it took me a year!

About a month ago, a friend of mine turned me on to your diet so I started following it. I lost 6 lb. in two weeks!

I know your diet definitely works if you follow it and it works very fast! It's great to see results in such a short time without very much effort at all! And the food is great! I have even invented some of my own recipes.

God Bless,
Georgina M., Shelby Township, MI

Dear Jay,

"I must thank you for The Fat Burning Diet, *which has gotten my body looking better than ever! I used to eat a high carbohydrate, low fat diet that kept me 'very plump'! I've learned more from your fat burning book than any of 50 books in my bodybuilding library. Thank you again!"*

—M.A. Hatfield, MA

Dear Jay,

Hello! My name is Max and I am writing on behalf of both myself and my identical twin brother, Mark. We read your book, The Fat Burning Diet, and loved it. We are fitness trainers, so diet is one of our biggest concerns. We've been on your program for only one month and can't believe the amazing results! We have always been lean, but now, according to our friends, we look like walking anatomy charts. Thank you for writing your book and may God bless you and your family.

—Max and Mark H., Los Angeles, CA

Dear Mr. Robb

"I assumed, like millions of Americans, that a high carbohydrate, low fat diet was the right one for me. After fours years of high carbohydrates and so little fat in my diet that my skin and hair looked like lizard and straw, I still clung to the accepted belief that if I followed the health community's and my doctor's advice, I would eventually lose weight and my body would be healthy.

But Oh, Contrare! I had actually gained weight on carbohydrates and my cholesterol was sky high. I was bloated, had gas all the time, had the energy level of dirt and my feet and ankles were so swollen from fluid retention I couldn't get my shoes on.

Then I read your book and started your diet. The first six days, I'd lost 5 pounds in just water and bloat and my energy level literally skyrocketed. I no longer needed a nap every afternoon and sleeping became a pleasurable night's rest instead of a wrestling match with my sheets. In just 4 weeks I'd lost 15 pounds!

To date I have lost 17 pounds and I'm grateful to you for creating a diet that actually works. For a 51 year old, overweight housewife with Meniere's disease that prevents me from exercising, this revelation of fat burning secrets has been a Godsend. I can't wait for your next book!"

—K.C., San Diego, CA

The Fat Burning Diet
COOK BOOK

Jay Robb, CCN, CFT

Certified Clinical Nutritionist
Certified Fitness Trainer

Loving Health Publications
in conjunction with

Enterprises, Inc.

1530 Encinitas Blvd.
Encinitas, CA 92024

jayrobb.com

Toll-free 1-877-JAY ROBB

Robb, Jay
The Fat Burning Diet COOK BOOK
Jay Robb

ISBN 0-9620608-7-9
1. Reducing diets. 2. Nutrition. 3. Diet—popular works.
4. Cooking.

Manufactured in the United States of America

Loving Health Publications
in conjuction with
Jay Robb Enterprises, Inc.
1530 Encinitas Blvd.
Encinitas, CA 92024

A Very Special Thank You To...

God for blessing my life with a wonderful family, success, happiness, health, wealth, fame, and inner peace. All that I am, do and will become...is You and only You.

My wife Rosemary for always being there for me and for always speaking up and insisting on the truth. My love deepens for you with each passing moment. And thank you for being my wife, my friend, and for making our home and our life a "spiritual" experience. I love you!

My son Angelo for just being you. That is enough. Your spirit and joy always shines bright and my love for you is greater with each passing day. Every moment I spend with you I will treasure for eternity.

Jeff Kahn, of Kahn Design, for creating the beautiful and outstanding cover design for my Cook Book. You are truly a talented artist! (Jeff may be reached at Kahn-Design.com)

My entire staff at Jay Robb Enterprises, Inc., and especially to Julie "Two-Tons-of-Fun" Teuton for being a great office manager; to "DrewMaster" Drew Goldstein, for creating our all new web site that is a true masterpiece and work of art; to Aaron Munshower for heading the shipping department that must handle the never-ending stream of orders we cast upon them.

My entire staff at Jay's Gym, and especially to "Captain" Kip Locke for doing a great job managing the club in my absence while I created this book; to Ryan Works for assisting Kip in running the club; to "Secret Asian Woman", Tori Ellis for joining our team and aligning with our mission; to "Killer" Kevin Feeney and "Thriller" Ingrid Saenger for being the two top personal trainers at our very special club.

ACKNOWLEDGMENTS:

Thanks to the following individuals and companies...

Kita Pelly (owner of KitaFit.com, author of, Maximum Power)
Thank you for your friendship, kindness, generosity and insights. And thank you for introducing me to Steve Weakley and the staff at KUSI Channel 9 News in San Diego. That introduction spawned my weekly TV segment, "The Fat Burning Chef", which led to this book and a whole new chapter in my life. Thank you, thank you, thank you!

Steve Weakley (News Producer at KUSI in San Diego)
Thank you for offering me the opportunity to create and perform each week, "The Fat Burning Chef", TV segment which was a hit from the start. And thank you for your friendship, insights, guidance and business advice...all of which are greatly appreciated. Your kindness and generosity are inspiring to me in my personal and business life.

Lisa Schwager (Program Director for KUSI News)
Thank you for all your help and support in creating and producing "The Fat Burning Chef". It is a pleasure to work with you each week and with Misha DiBono, Dan Plante and the entire staff at KUSI.

To All Health Stores, Gyms, Nutrition Centers and Doctors
Thank you for all your support and for carrying my books, protein powders and product line. A special thanks to "Jimbo" Someck of Jimbo's...Naturally!; Nancy Hughey, Natural Living Corporate Manager of Henry's Marketplace; and to all the Whole Foods, Wild Oats stores, Claudia's, Mother's Market and every store, gym, nutrition center and doctor that carries our products. Your endless support is greatly appreciated. Thank you all!

Author's Note

"To get lean and fit, the very best exercise program is almost useless unless you adhere to a diet that targets your own bodyfat."

The author does not claim to be a doctor or healer of any sort. This book is intended for educational purposes only and should not be used as a guide for diagnosis and treatment of any disease. If you have any health problems, it is advisable to seek the advice of a health care professional of your choice.

Wife: How do you like the rabbit stew I fixed for dinner.

Husband: It tastes great but I just found a hare on my plate.

A Special Note to You:

It is no coincidence that this book is in your hands right now. It has come to you offering hope, promise and a new way of life...a life that is filled with energy and aspirations.

CONTENTS

CHAPTERS:

"Only two groups of people fall for flattery—men and women."

Introduction

About a week ago, my wife was driving down the freeway while doing her knitting. In southern California, most drivers are usually speeding down the interstate while talking on their cell phone...but not so for my wife. She was knitting.

With knitting needles in her hands, obviously my wife wasn't paying very close attention to her driving and was going over the speed limit. Then without realizing it, my wife passed a motorcycle cop who turned on his flashing red lights and quickly went after her.

Because my wife was going so fast, it took the police officer several minutes to get right on her tailgate. But my wife was busy and didn't see the red lights or the officer who was right on her rear bumper. She just kept on knitting.

The motorcycle cop quickly realized my wife didn't see his red lights flashing in her rearview mirror, so he accelerated and pulled along side of her window. With a circular hand motion, the officer finally caught my wife's attention and motioned her to roll down the window.

My wife rolled down the window and the angry officer yelled at the top of his lungs, "PULLOVER!" To this my wife smiled, held up her knitting and yelled back, "No, it's a SWEATER!"

So often we are driving down the highway of life "knitting" and not paying attention to our journey, nor to what we are eating. Then, as time passes by, the excess fat accumulates and suddenly makes us aware that a change is needed. This book contains the "changes" you can make in your eating habits so that you can attain the body of your dreams, even if you have little-time for exercise. And it's fun and easy with my delicious recipes!

About Jay Robb

Jay Robb was born June 15, 1953.
He is a Certified Clinical Nutritionist and a Certified Fitness Trainer
with over 20 years of experience
as a professional in his field. He is
the CEO of Jay Robb Enterprises,
Inc., a company that produces cut-
ting-edge nutritional supplements
which are sold worldwide. He is
the owner of Jay's Gym in the San
Diego area and is a feature colum-
nist for Natural Bodybuilding magazine, and a contributing writer
for Men's Exercise, Women's Exercise, and Exercise For Men
Only.

Jay Robb is also the TV Host for "The Fat Burning Chef", seen
every Sunday morning on KUSI Channel 9 in San Diego. He is
the author of six popular health and fitness books including his
top seller, *The Fat Burning Diet*, which was created in 1991 and
started the low-carb, high protein diet revolution that has taken
the country by storm.

Jay also has served as a consultant to Kent Johnston, the former
Strength Coach for the Green Bay Packers and has helped tens of
thousands of individuals over the past two decades lose weight
and gain energy like never before. Jay Robb lives in La Costa, a
beach community on San Diego's beautiful north coast. He is
happily married and has a 12 year old son.

To discover more about Jay Robb and his company, please visit
their web site at: **jayrobb.com**

"It is in silence, that all can be heard."

"I recently lost twenty pounds. Unfortunately, I was in England at the time"
—Daniel Lybra

CHAPTER 1

What You Should Know First?

The Fat Burning Diet was created because of my need for a diet to end my long-time and silent bout with a medical condition termed as "reactive hypoglycemia". This is a pre-diabetic condition, I developed in the 1970s, that forces one's moods and energy levels to rise and fall like the world's largest rollercoaster. One minute I was on top of the world, the next moment I was tired, depressed and living in fear.

By 1978 I was a wreck. I looked great on the outside but on the inside my emotions were as fragile as a blown glass swan. I felt like my nerves had been grated until they were raw. Crying became my spontaneous emotion of choice. I could cry at the drop of a hat, yet I had no clue why I was crying. I had no real reason to be sad...I just was. To be blunt, I was a mess and I thought I was losing my mind.

In the midst of a full decade of serious blood sugar problems, my body finally gave in and my energy levels dropped to a point near zero. I hit the "bottom" in 1978 and that experience is described in my book, The Fat Burning Diet. Totally running out of energy and being physically and mentally exhausted was a devastating feeling. I was living each day with barely enough energy to drag my tired-buns out of bed.

While laying flat on my back, unable to get up one day, I knew I had hit bottom and needed help. So I put my hands together and said a prayer...not an ordinary prayer...but a REAL prayer from my heart as I completely surrendered for help. The room was spinning, I was crying and I felt there was no hope left in my life. I honestly knew of no way to stop my mind from being depressed, scared and confused. But when I put my hands together and prayed, something magical happened. The room stopped spinning and my energy level returned. So I prayed hard and asked for the answers to my problems. And I promised that if I was shown the way back to perfect health, I would tell the world of my discoveries.

Just prior to my ego-cleansing, physical collapse (because of my lack of energy and bouts with depression), I had scheduled an appointment with my family doctor to check me over completely. Miraculously, after a complete exam, my doctor couldn't find anything physically wrong with me. In fact, he said I appeared to be in great shape. He felt I was simply under a lot of stress, so he prescribed a stomach calming drug and sent me to see a psychologist. Was I going crazy?

Three visits with the psychologist had me drag all the skeletons out of the closet, only to discover I really liked both my parents, I was happy deep inside, I wasn't sexually frustrated, I wasn't angry, bitter, abused as a child, or experiencing anything else that could have made me so exhausted and depressed.

During the fourth visit with my therapist, "I" began to ask the questions and take control of the session. I looked at her and said, "Obviously my past is not a mess and I am not harboring any anger, hatred or resentment toward my parents, sisters or friends. I have been doing a lot of research and have discovered that one's diet can produce anxiety, depression, fear and a whole host of other emotions I am currently experiencing, so this is my last session with you.

My therapist just stared at me in disbelief, not uttering a single word. The room went deadly silent as if she was at a total loss for words or a professional response. Finally, after what seemed like an eternity, my therapist spoke, but her words were voiced in disbelief of my discoveries. "Jay, we are just starting to make progress, so let's stay focused", she remarked. "You seem to be eating healthy...just look at your big muscles and great body, so there must be more to it", she added sternly. "I'm sure that diet is only a small part of your problem, so please don't start fishing in the dark and obsess over this idea", she added.

After sitting there, once again listening to my therapist, I just shook my head and said, "No, this is not in my head. In fact...I'm sure it is not, so I'm leaving right now." To this my therapist quickly replied, "If you leave now you're crazy!" Laughing out loud at such a ridiculous and potentially intimidating remark, I stood up and said, "I'm not crazy. My problems appear to stem more from my diet than from what I am thinking or how I was raised as a child." I then waved good-bye and left her office, never to return.

It took guts to stand up for what I felt in my heart...and it felt so right to walk out of that office. As I walked away I realized there must be thousands and thousands of others who are in therapy, and the root of their problem may stem from their diet. I then realized that one must first follow the best diet and life-style possible...if all their problems don't clear up, THEN go see a therapist, psychiatrist or psychologist for mental and emotional help and support. Currently in America it seems to be the other way around.

30 days after I walked-out on my therapist, and after much prayer and searching, I discovered a new doctor who was a Preventative Medical Physician and he diagnosed me with severe reactive hypoglycemia and helped me organize my diet and eliminate many foods I was allergic to. I instantly felt better and have never had a serious blood sugar dip since. To make a long story short, my

prayers were answered, so I set out to spend the rest of my life telling the world about the diet and health secrets I had discovered (which was my end of the bargain).

Since 1978, I have learned a great deal about diet. As a Certified Clinical Nutritionist, I have been able to apply this knowledge to countless others who are in need of this vital information. America is on a blood sugar rollercoaster ride and I'm often the only guy they can turn to when they want to get off. And I have been able to seriously help people afflicted with diabetes, hypoglycemia, chronic fatigue, Candida, as well as healthy, fit people who want to gain energy, get leaner and stay that way.

With my roots in bodybuilding, I also am an expert in getting bodyfat levels down to 5% or less in preparation for a bodybuilding competition. My diet principles are so accurate that I can get almost anyone ready for a show in as-little-as 10 short weeks. It's easy once you understand the glycogen loading principles (GLP) of my diet.

As you will see, my diet is not a low-carb or a high-carb diet. It is both! My diet focuses on lean meats, fresh eggs, raw nuts and seeds, gluten-free whole grains (rice or millet), and plenty of fresh fruits and vegetables, which is exactly what is required for an outstandingly healthy body. If excess bodyfat is clinging to you and poor health is knocking at your door, it simply means you must immediately and radically increase your intake of fresh, whole foods...PERIOD! There is no way around it.

Take it Off! Take it ALL Off! My Challenge...
It is my feeling that a diet authority or guru should practice what they preach and the diet he or she advocates should work FOR THEM. Currently I see many best selling diet books on the bookshelves, yet I am hard-pressed to find any of the authors to be lean. In fact, they don't usually ever mention their own bodyfat

levels...and I have almost never seen any of them in a swimsuit, or with their shirts off. Show us your abs guys and gals! I say contact all the authors of the top-selling diet books and give each author 3-5 days advance notice to appear on stage on a national TV show. Then, while we are all on the show, ask each of us to demonstrate how well our diet works by revealing our own body. Simple request. The old saying, "The proof is in the pudding", really applies here. If all these diets are so great, let's see it! My diet works, and I'll be happy to show anyone how my body looks. But will any other authors? Only the ones who have diets that really work (which will be the ones who show up for the challenge).

While I doubt if very many other authors would meet my challenge, you as a consumer need to be aware that many authors hide away because they can't get lean on their own diet. If they can't get lean, how do they expect YOU to get lean? You figure it out. I'm here to speak and show you the truth, the whole truth and nothing but the truth. If you don't find my diet program to be the best program you have ever experienced, then simply ask for a refund and you will get it. Since I first developed my Fat Burning Diet plan in 1991, all the returned books could fit on one small shelf in our offices! Folks, my program is that good! And now it is time for you to experience it...and this book offers you the exact information you need and some new twists to the diet, as well as a boat-load of mouth watering recipes. Please read on and enjoy! As always, should you need anything or would like me to perform a seminar/workshop for your club, organization or corporation, or wish to schedule a private phone or office consultation with me, call our offices in the San Diego area at 1-877 JAY ROBB, or contact us on-line at jayrobb.com.

"Last week, my wife had just finished waxing the floors when she heard our son opening the front door. She shouted, "Be careful on that floor Angelo. It's just been waxed." Angelo went ahead and walked right in and replied, "Don't worry, Mom, I'm wearing my cleats."

CHAPTER 2

Real Fat Burning Secrets

*"Some people will believe anything
if it is whispered to them."*

In 1991 I wrote the original manuscript for my now famous "high-carb / low-carb" diet book, The Fat Burning Diet. I feel that book sparked the low-carb diet revolution that America is currently experiencing. And now, many, many low-carb books have flooded the bookstore shelves, each expressing their own version of what I originally reintroduced to the American people. My hat goes off to many of these doctors and nutritionists who realized my "controlled carbohydrate" diet plan was extremely effective, and jumped on the bandwagon. With the combined efforts of various low-carb diet authorities, we have seriously halted the high carbohydrate, low-fat diet stronghold that was helping make the USA one of the fattest nations in the world. Hallelujah!

My Fat Burning Diet has remained unique in many ways, when compared to most of the low-carb ONLY diet programs and high-carb ONLY diets that are currently on the market. My plan has an individual consuming low-carb meals at certain times and high-carb, low-fat meals at other times, so a person actually gets the best of both worlds...low-carbs and high carbs! The Fat Burning Diet is based on a simply glycogen (muscle starch) loading and depleting technique I call GLP (Glycogen Loading Principle). If glycogen levels are full, then carbohydrate is restricted. Once glycogen levels are depleted (through exercise and/or carbohydrate restriction) then carbohydrates are consumed. It can't get much simpler than that!

The Fat Burning Diet's simple glycogen loading/depleting principle makes this style of eating suitable for nearly EVERYONE! A typical low-carb diet is usually only suitable for weight loss for a short time in sedentary or moderately active individuals. And the typical high-carbohydrate, low fat diet is usually only suitable for EXTREMELY active individuals and endurance athletes. Because of the low-carb/high-carb eating principles, The Fat Burning Diet is ideal for athletes, bodybuilders, triathletes, marathon runners, and active individuals, as well as sedentary folks. My diet even works for those who totally avoid exercise. And it is all because of my glycogen loading and depleting principles. (See The Fat Burning Diet for more details on this principle).

I now offer you The Fat Burning Diet Cook Book. All recipes in this book are compatible with my Fat Burning Diet program. You will find oodles of delicious recipes for carb-depleting, and carb-loading. The Fat Burning Diet is so easy to live with for life, mainly because I allow low-carb and high-carb meals to be part of the plan. In fact, unless you are diabetic, I insist that you carb-load regularly to replenish glycogen levels and avoid ketosis. (If you are diabetic, please follow the "Diabetic Plan" outlined in, The Fat Burning Diet.)

Ketosis is a radical state of fat burning that only happens once ALL carbohydrate reserves are depleted and the body has no choice but to create and burn ketone bodies from available bodyfat and fat from foods in the diet. On The Fat Burning Diet program, carb-loading is utilized just prior to going into deep ketosis, thus fat burning takes place, but your body can maintain its glycogen reserves, and in general, is a much happier camper,

When a marathon runner is training, glycogen levels are usually depleted each day he or she runs. When glycogen levels get too low, the body begins to go into ketosis and at that point the runner will "hit the wall", meaning he or she is out of carbohydrate reserves and the body will now draw on fat stores exclusively. To a runner "glycogen debt" can take place at the 18 to 23 mile mark of a marathon, unless proper glycogen loading, carbohydrate replenishing and special fat burning techniques are utilized.

"Hitting the wall" can be devastating to an athlete. He or she will feel like their legs are made of soft rubber, and their energy levels are zip! On a typical ketogenic, low-carb diet, you can also "hit the wall", WITHOUT running even one mile. Dietary induced ketosis happens through carb-depletion and may take up to three days to occur. The marathon runner can deplete ALL carbohydrate reserves in a matter of 3-5 hours through vigorous running, while a ketogenic dieter will achieve glycogen depletion in a period of several days (unless they are also exercising strenuously).

Deep ketosis is not usually a pleasant state to go into; but being in ketosis is actually quite comfortable. The problem with ketosis is the going into and coming out of that state which can make a person feel light headed, a bit grumpy and radically crave sweets as the body makes the switch to burning ketones. So, on The Fat Burning Diet, ketosis is monitored and avoided for the most part.

On The Fat Burning Diet, you learn to deplete your glycogen levels until they become low, at which time you use a carb-loading meal to fully replenish glycogen levels. If glycogen levels become extremely low, and/or the person is very active, it may require a series of high-carb, low-fat meals to refill glycogen levels, which is a technique I also outline in my ladies only book, Maximum Power...which I co-authored with friend, colleague and fitness expert, Kita Pelly. Fat burning takes place readily, but deep ketosis is primarily avoided.

For a sedentary person, low-carb meals may need to be followed for 2-3 days before a high carb meal, or series of meals, needs to be eaten. For an endurance athlete, carb-depletion may only require a day or less, before carb-loading again with a high-carb meal or series of meals. Carb-depletion and carb-loading are all based upon energy expenditures that vary from individual to individual. The key is to learn your signals that indicate your body is nearly out of carbohydrate reserves. Those signals are as follows:

1. Mood swings.
2. Fatigue.
3. Mild depression.
4. Mental confusion.
5. Carbohydrate craving, usually for sweets.
6. Feeling light-headed.
7. Energy slumps.
8. The muscles feel flat and deflated.

As you near ketosis, any one or all of the above symptoms may appear. If you are experiencing these typical symptoms, be aware that you may have carb-depleted too long and are now going into ketosis. To stop from taking the "ketosis plunge" (as I call it) simply eat one to five high carbohydrate meals to help refill glycogen levels (there are many great and very healthy high carbohydrate recipes listed in this book).

There is an easy way to test for ketosis...
To avoid taking the "ketosis plunge" you can simply test for ketones in your urine. Ketosis testing is performed using a Ketostix®. To test your urine after carb-depleting for one to three days, run a test strip through your urine, at midstream, and wait for the strip to change color. If the Ketostix® turns light pink, then you are nearing ketosis and are almost out of glycogen reserves. If the Ketostix® turns light purple or deep purple then you are going into heavy ketosis and are out of glycogen reserves entirely.

While it is ideal to begin carb-loading just before the Ketostix® turns pink, you may sometimes go into total ketosis (the stick turns purple) before you realize it. That is OK, and just indicates it is time to eat carbohydrates for the next one to five meals until your glycogen levels are filled again. Then you simply start the process over again by carb-depleting until the sticks turn pink, then you begin carb-loading, etc., etc. It is really that simple and easy.

What if I have carb-depleted but my Ketostix won't turn pink or purple?

Ketostix® are a general guideline to indicate when a newcomer to dieting and exercise has completely reduced carbohydrate reserves to the point where the body must begin to burn fat exclusively. Ketostix® are not infallible, so they do not work for everyone, every time.

Ketostix® are best utilized by beginners to my diet plan, and those who are not in top physical condition. Someone who has been exercising regularly for years may be a very efficient fat burner, therefore can burn ketones very efficiently. When ketones are burned efficiently, they will not show up in the urine. On the other hand, a novice to exercise and weight loss will not be an efficient fat burner, therefor, he or she will not burn ketones effectively and unburned or partially burned ketones will be excreted as waste from the body via the urine, hence the unburned ketones are easily detected with a Ketostix®.

When a novice fat burner becomes an efficient fat burner, he or she can no longer rely on Ketostix® for carb-depletion detection. For long term dieting success, it is ideal to learn the physical and mental signs (as listed earlier) your body is displaying that indicates you are nearing or in ketosis. Once you are in tune with your body it is easy to sense when you are almost out of carbohydrate reserves. And once you realize you are almost depleted,

you simply start consuming carbohydrate based meals until your glycogen reserves are full once again, then repeat the process.
If you have been active and carb-depleting for over three days, and the Ketostix® is not changing colors, then please check the following:

1. Are you eating too much carbohydrate on your carb-depletion days? 30 to 100 grams of carbs daily, is usually plenty unless you are extremely active.
2. Are you an efficient fat burner from past dieting or from performing an abundance of cardiovascular exercises for the past several months or longer?
3. Are you active enough to deplete your glycogen reserves?

Should you discover that you are carb-depleting properly and the Ketostix® won't change colors, then you must get in tune with your body and begin to carb-load when you feel your body is carb-depleted. In general, most individuals I have worked with need to carb-load after 1-3 days of carb-depletion. This time varies with activity levels and the severity of carbohydrate restriction. Eating 30 grams or less of carbohydrate each day and being active may deplete glycogen levels in as-little-as 6 to 24 hours. Eating 60 grams of carbohydrate daily and being active may deplete glycogen levels in 24 to 36 hours. Eating 80 grams of carbs daily and being active may deplete glycogen levels in 36 to 48 hours, but you need to determine your own needs by watching for the signs that indicate you are nearing glycogen debt.

The carb-loading phase can occur in two ways on The Fat Burning Diet. The traditional way, as outlined in my Fat Burning Diet book, is to eat moderately low-carbohydrate meals for a little over two and a half days, then a high-carbohydrate meal is consumed to replenish some of the diminished glycogen. This technique is based on the principle of only partially depleting glycogen levels and then topping them off with a high-carb meal, eaten in the evening three times a week. But I have a technique I discovered many years ago when working with bodybuilders that appears to work fantastic for nearly everyone who tries it and can produce radical weight loss/fat loss to take place!

An all new Fat Burning Diet carb-loading/depleting principle outlined in this Cook Book will suggest the average female consume approximately 200-300 total grams of natural carbohydrates and the average male taking in 300 - 400 total grams of natural carbohydrates, before the carb-loading phase is complete and carb-depletion begins again. This carb-loading phase may require up to five, or more, consecutive meals to effectively accomplish. It is best to eat the carbs over a series of meals instead of at one big meal because glycogen can load better over a longer period of time.

It is not commonly known or expressed by many low-carb diet gurus, but the average adult male or female can store approximately 350 to 400 grams of carbohydrate in their muscles and liver as glycogen. This means that once you are almost depleted of glycogen (from eating low-carb meals, and/or exercising vigorously) you can eat 350 to 400 grams of carbohydrate, and any excess carbs you can't burn will become glycogen, NOT fat. Some low-carb diet advocates erroneously teach that all excess carbs can become fat, but the truth is, you have plenty of room for error.

Once glycogen is depleted, it may require that you eat four baked potatoes, two cups of rice and three big yams to fully replenish your reserves. The key to success is to carb-load for a series of meals until glycogen levels are full, then switch back to low-carb meals until you have almost fully depleted them once again, then repeat. For some individuals to get in 350 or more grams of carbohydrate may require one or TWO days of high carb meals to accomplish. No matter how long it takes to load the muscles with glycogen, once they are full you MUST switch back to low carb eating until glycogen levels are once again diminished. Then the cycle begins again. It's that easy.

If you are exercising, I have great news! Those who exercise vigorously and do cardiovascular training (aerobics, running, biking, swimming, etc.) can sometimes store 2-3 times as much glycogen as a sedentary person. This higher level of glycogen capacity is primarily due to the body's adaptation principle to training and carb-depletion and carb-loading. In other words, your body will simply adapt to the carb-loading and carb-depleting by increasing its capacity to store glycogen, thus giving you a greater reserve to draw from.

A trained athlete, can often store 800 to 900 (or more) grams of carbohydrate as glycogen. Once glycogen levels are depleted, it may require two full days (or longer) of carb-loading meals to replenish the glycogen levels to maximum capacity. This principle is also used when I train bodybuilders to prepare for a contest.

Beginning 10 weeks out for a bodybuilding show, I will have a bodybuilder eat 2 days of low-carb meals, followed by one full day of carb-loading meals. This creates a natural increase in glycogen storage capacity, and also allows for an "anabolic" insulin spike to occur during the carb-loading phase. Then, two days before the contest, I have the bodybuilder begin carb-loading at noon and continue carb-loading all the way to show time. This carb-depleting, carb-loading technique insures that maximum glycogen is retained in the muscles on the day of the show, thus creating the illusion that the bodybuilder has much larger muscles, when in reality the extra size is glycogen. The final carb-loading phase also fills the veins with more water (carrying the extra glucose) and causes the veins to become full and extremely visible. And all this was accomplished through the proper use of low-carb and high-carb meals and allows a female athlete to step on stage with a mere 6-8% bodyfat and male athlete to step on stage with a bodyfat level of only 4-5%!

I have a theory about human evolution. My theory is that we have evolved to survive in extreme conditions and during times of famine. Evolutionary survival would see the human race eating a lot of calories when food was in abundance, and eating very little calories when food was scarce. This naturally produced a lean body that was efficient at surviving while hunting and gathering food. It also produced a natural carb-loading and carb-depleting cycle that followed the seasons, climate and food gathering ability. One day might find a human gorging on fresh fruit in season, the next day, the same human is foraging for a small animal to eat and running on fat and glycogen-reserves. And The Fat Burning Diet follows these simple evolutionary patterns that we have adapted to for countless centuries.

Please note that, The Fat Burning Diet Cook Book, is primarily void of the problem carbohydrate foods that many millions of Americans may be sensitive to or allergic to, often because they contain a protein called gluten. These foods include wheat, rye, oats, barley, and most other grains except millet, rice, and corn. Also, due to its potential allergenic properties for some individuals, recipes that contain milk or dairy products should be avoided or the dairy portion should be substituted with soy milk or soy cheese or simply omit the dairy portion of the recipe altogether.

Note: Whole wheat and many whole grains contain gluten, which many, many individuals are allergic to, thus gluten containing foods are only used in a few of the recipes in this book. Most people can tolerate wheat and gluten containing foods once per week, so do not over consume these foods. When whole wheat is refined into white flour, much of the gluten is milled out with the wheat germ, thus refined wheat is less nutritious but far less allergenic. In the case of sprouted grain bread that is flourless, these breads are very low in gluten because the sprouting process converts the indigestible gluten into a digestible nutrient during the sprouting process.

It is also important to note that The Fat Burning Diet is centered around three main food groups that are used for carb-depleting: a) proteins, b) vegetables, and c) natural fats. To replenish glycogen we carb-load with low-fat, natural carbohydrate foods such as potatoes, yams, winter squash, rice, corn, millet and fresh fruit. Please note that sugar, honey, barley malt, rice syrup, fruit juice concentrates, malto-dextrin, and all refined sugars and sweeteners are severely limited or completely eliminated on The Fat Burning Diet because they can cause a serious blood sugar/insulin spike and can feed Candida (yeast overgrowth) in susceptible individuals. In place of high glycemic sugars we use Agave, which is the juice of the Blue Agave Cactus (the same cactus used to make Tequila). Agave is rated only 11 on the glycemic index, making it safe to use as a sweetener, yet has a very pleasant, sweet taste very similar to a mild honey.

You may also notice that there are no recipes that call for the artificial sweetener known as aspartame, simply because there appears to be research indicating aspartame may cause health problems in some individuals (and the stuff gives me a headache every time I consume it). Instead, for a non-caloric, no-carbohydrate sweet taste we use the herb Stevia, which is "natural" and delightful when combined with certain foods. (More on Agave and Stevia in the next chapter.)

Two Simple Fat Burning Tips...

Fat Burning Tip #1 - Whether you are on a low-carb day or a high-carb day, it is best to stop eating 2-3 hours before you go to bed each night. This will allow the food to digest before retiring for the evening and insure that you get a good-night's sleep. Also, by not eating before bed, insulin will be in check and your body can effectively burn fat as you sleep.

Fat Burning Tip #2 - It is ideal to allow 12 hours to elapse each day where no food is consumed. This translates to 12 hours of eating and 12 hours of fasting. This pattern of eating is easiest to accomplish by noting the time you consume your last meal of the day, and then waiting 12 hours until you eat you first meal of the next day.

An example of the two previous fat burning tips would be eating your last meal of the day at 9:00 PM, then you go to sleep at 11:30 PM. When you get up the next day, do not eat or drink anything except water until 9:00 AM., at which time you may have a meal or snack (whichever fits your schedule and life-style).

And so, I offer you my favorite recipes, along with many more that my friends, associates, family and Fat Burning Diet followers have kindly shared with me over the past 20 years. I love to eat. If you also love to eat, yet want to stay lean for life, then I offer you three final words about using my unique recipe book...INDULGE AND ENJOY!

*"Middle age can be a time when a narrow
waist and a broad mind trade places."*

CHAPTER 3

What You Need To Prepare the Recipes

It is ideal, but not mandatory that you stock your kitchen ahead of time with everything you need to prepare the delicious recipes contained in this book. Below is a list of items you will want to have on hand.

1. Basic kitchen utensils: Sharp knives, a blender, electric beaters, grater, colander, a variety of non-stick pans, a variety of baking dishes, several large mixing spoons, measuring spoons, one or two measuring cups, a vegetable peeler, a can opener, a spatula, and a variety of large and small mixing bowls.

2. Basic cooking and baking ingredients: Non-stick cooking spray, rice flour, olive oil, Agave, Stevia (liquid is best), rice bran, flax seeds, flax seed powder, flax seed oil, frozen strawberries, a variety of natural flavorings, a variety of cooking spices and herbs, apple cider vinegar, Bragg's Liquid Aminos, whole peppercorns and pepper grinder, natural "real" butter, various flavors of whey protein, unsweetened low-carb vanilla and chocolate egg protein powder, unsweetened low-carb vanilla flavored soy protein powder, free-range whole eggs, egg whites, 100% flourless sprouted and unsalted bread, brown rice, millet, raw almonds, and whole garlic cloves. (Also see my "Grocery List" of what you need on page 192.)

"A fish is an underwater creature that grows fastest between the time it is caught and the time the fisherman describes it."

Chapter 4

Shopping For Ingredients

Many of the foods listed in my recipe book may be found at your local grocery store. Most of the specialty items, such as Agave, protein powders, brown rice, flourless bread, almonds, millet, Bragg's Liquid Aminos, apple cider vinegar and flax seed oil, can often only be found at your local health food store (or purchased from a natural food mail-order company).

Buy Organically Grown Foods and
Hormone-Free Meats Whenever Possible

When purchasing produce or any food item it is ideal to buy organically grown whenever it is available. When buying meats, choose hormone-free. When buying eggs, choose ones laid by free-range and hormone-free chickens. Organically grown foods are raised without the use of harmful chemical pesticides and are fertilized naturally with compost, and natural organic fertilizers. The combination of growing food in nutrient rich soil and not spraying or treating the food with chemical pesticides, can produce a very nutrient rich, non-toxic food source that can be far superior to foods grown using conventional farming methods. To discover more about the benefits of organic farming methods, free-range eggs and hormone-free meat, ask your local health food store for books and materials on the subject.

A Special Note About All the Recipes:

In general, each recipe (unless otherwise stated) can be utilized as a meal (or snack if specified) for one large framed person or divided in half to feed two smaller framed individuals. Some individuals may naturally weight 200+ pounds and others may weigh a mere 100 pounds, so use the recipes according to your appetite, body-size, and calorie needs.

For your own knowledge, the protein, fat, carbohydrate and calorie content is listed for each recipe.

Enough with the preparation phase. Let's move on to the recipes...

Chapter 5

What's For Breakfast?

The term breakfast is derived from the expression, "breaking the fast", meaning the eating of food after a period of abstinence (fasting). This "fasting" period is usually during a good-night's-sleep, and the fast is broken sometime during the morning that follows.

As stated earlier in this book, it is ideal to allow 12 full hours to pass, since your last meal of the previous day, before consuming breakfast. This will allow more time to burn fat and can improve your digestion and elimination.

Breakfast can be simple and easy, or complex and elaborate. On high carb days, you can begin your day with fresh fruit, or eggs and hash browns, or any other variety of natural carbohydrate foods. On low-carb days, you can utilize mostly protein based foods. On the pages to follow I have revealed over 150 of my favorite recipes, many of which I have utilized for the past 25 years of my life with great success.

Low-Carb Breakfasts

"Sunshine Eggs and Cheese"

Protein: 30g
Fat: 19g
Carbohydrate: 3g
Calories: 314

This breakfast is quick, powerful, high in protein and delicious!
The combination of eggs and cheese is outstanding in protein,
calcium, magnesium, iron, essential fatty acids and many other
nutrients.

Ingredients needed:
5 egg whites and 2 yolks
1 tsp. olive oil
1oz. grated mozzarella cheese

Heat a non-stick skillet to low-medium heat and pour in the
olive oil and wipe with a paper towel to evenly coat the pan.
Crack the eggs, one at a time separating the whites from the
yolks until you have 5 eggs whites and only 2 yolks in the
skillet. Cover the skillet with a lid and cook slowly until the
whites are solid and the yolks are runny, but lightly firm on the
edges. Slide the eggs onto a plate, then cover the eggs evenly
with the mozzarella cheese. Grab your fork and enjoy. If I am
still hungry following the above meal, I will consume a whey
protein drink contain 1 oz. of protein blended into 6 oz. of pure
water. For a "lighter" breakfast, try 2-3 whites and 1 yolk,
topped with 1 oz. of mozzarella cheese.

*A woman called the utility company and
complained that her electricity was out.
What should she do? The voice on the
other end quickly advised, "Open your
freezer, and eat the ice cream."*

"A Beefy Breakfast"

Protein: 65g
Fat: 20g
Carbohydrate: 7g
Calories: 491

Ingredients:
6 oz. 7% fat, lean ground sirloin
1 oz. slice of mozzarella cheese
1/4 onion (chopped)

In a bowl combine the ground sirloin with the onion and mix by
hand until the onion is well blended into the meat. Form the
meat into one large patty about 3/4 of an inch thick and place
in a medium heated skillet or grill. Cook until lightly brown then
flip the patty and continue cooking until both sides are brown
and the middle is no longer pink. Place the cheese slice on top
of the patty about 1 minute before the patty is completely
cooked. This will lightly melt the cheese. Remove from the
skillet when done and place on plate. For a spicy breakfast, top
with 1-2 tbs. of fresh salsa.

*When my son Angelo was a little boy I
would read him bedtime stories. One
evening I was reading "Goldilocks and the
Three Bears" when my son looked up at
me and said, "Is that porridge made with
all natural ingredients?"*

"Out-of-this-World Omelet"

Protein: 31g
Fat: 19g
Carbohydrate: 8g
Calories: 336

Ingredients:
5 whole eggs (discard 3 yolks)
1/2 small zucchini (cut into thin half slices)
1/2 small red pepper (seeds removed and chopped)
1 oz. grated mozzarella cheese
1 tsp. olive oil

In a lightly oil skillet, saute the zucchini and red pepper until
tender, then set aside. In a bowl, whip the eggs together then
pour into a medium heated, lightly oiled, non-stick skillet and
add the zucchini and red pepper. Cook until eggs are solid and
firm then top with cheese, fold over the omelet in half and slide
onto a plate. Enjoy!

Recently we hired a young man to work at Jay's Gym. On the new employee's first day our Manager handed him a broom and told him his first job was to sweep the front sidewalk. "But," the new employee said, "I'm a college graduate." "I'm sorry I didn't know that," replied our Manager. "Give me the broom and I'll show you how."

Huevos (Eggs) Mexican-Style

Protein: 32g
Fat: 23g
Carbohydrate: 10g
Calories: 368

Ingredients:
5 egg whites and 2 yolks (beaten in a bowl)
1 oz. Alpine Lace low-sodium, low-fat cheese
1/4 medium Haas avocado (cubed)
2 tbs. fresh or bottled salsa
1 tbs. fresh cilantro leaves
1 small mild green Chile pepper (diced)
1 tsp. olive oil

Heat a large non-stick skillet on medium then add the olive oil (or spray with a non-stick spray). Pour in the eggs and green Chile pepper. Cook like an omelet until eggs are firm then place the 1 oz. slice of cheese on top and fold the eggs in half to form a half circle that pockets the cheese. Slide off onto a plate and top with cilantro, salsa and avocado. This is truly an awesome breakfast!

*Customer: "Waitress, why is my doughnut
all smashed?"
Waitress: "You said you wanted a cup of
coffee and a doughnut, and step on it!"*

Basic Pizza Omelet

Protein: 20g
Fat: 20g
Carbohydrate: 3g
Calories: 279

Ingredients:
2 whole eggs (whipped in a bowl)
1 tsp. olive oil
1 tbs. pizza sauce
1 oz. mozzarella cheese

In a skillet heated to medium, pour in the olive oil and wipe
evenly over the pan with a paper towel. Pour in the whipped
eggs and tilt the pan until the eggs cover the bottom of the pan.
Cook until the eggs are firm (about 1-2 minutes) then slide the
cooked eggs onto a plate, cover with pizza sauce and top with
mozzarella cheese. If you prefer melted cheese, slip the Pizza
Omelet into the microwave for 10-30 seconds. This is an
incredible taste sensation for breakfast and for those who love
pizza but want to stay lean.

"The energy crisis is really bad here in southern California. During a recent power blackout, I was stuck on an escalator for three hours."

Pizza Omelet Supreme

Protein: 39g
Fat: 29g
Carbohydrate: 6g
Calories: 350

Ingredients:
2 whole eggs (whipped in a bowl)
1 tsp. olive oil
1 tbs. pizza sauce
1 oz. mozzarella cheese
2 oz. ground sirloin (cooked and browned in a pan)
1/8 white onion (diced)
3 black olives (sliced thin)

Cook the ground sirloin with the onion, turn off the heat and set aside. In a skillet heated to medium, pour in the olive oil and wipe evenly over the pan with a paper towel. Pour in the whipped eggs and tilt the pan until the eggs cover the bottom of the pan. Cook until the eggs are firm (about 1-2 minutes) then slide the cooked eggs onto a plate, cover with pizza sauce, ground sirloin and top with mozzarella cheese and black olives. If you prefer melted cheese, slip the Pizza Omelet Supreme into the microwave for 10-30 seconds.

*"The safest way to double your money is to
fold it over once and put it in your pocket."*

Turkey Bacon and Eggs

Protein: 31g
Fat: 23g
Carbohydrate: 3g
Calories: 355

Ingredients:
4 egg whites
2 egg yolks
3 strips turkey bacon (purchase at your local health food store)

In a non-stick skillet, cook the turkey bacon until it is crisp, then place the strips on a plate covered with a paper towel. Take an additional paper towel and pat the top of the strips to blot out any excess oil and fat. In the same pan used to cook the bacon, cook the egg whites and yolks sunny side up with the pan covered. This will cook the whites and only partially cook the yolks. Slide the cooked eggs from the pan onto a plate, then accompany the eggs with the bacon and prepare to enjoy a long-standing American tradition...minus the toast, of course.

High-Carb Breakfasts

For carb-loading meals and/or carb-loading days, breakfast can be fun, delicious and energizing...as long as you follow my Fat Burning Diet principles. When you carb-load at any meal except the last meal of the day, it is critical that you consume 2-3 oz. of a lean or low-fat protein source FIRST, before you consume your carbohydrate portion of the meal. By consuming the protein first you delay an insulin response, while flooding your bloodstream with a complete amino acid pool that blocks the amino acid Tryptophan from reaching the brain in high concentration. Should the amino acid Tryptophan reach the brain in concentration, (as usually happens at a high carbohydrate only based meal), then the Tryptophan is converted to the brain chemical neurotransmitter "serotonin" which immediately causes you to become mildly sedated, sleepy, lethargic and feel very relaxed...none of which are the best way to start your day. But there is one exception to this high carbohydrate rule...

Fresh fruit, due to its high fructose concentration, will not reach the bloodstream fast enough to elicit a massive insulin response that drives Tryptophan into the brain, thus you avoid the "serotonin sensation" that makes you sleepy and relaxed. When a fruit only breakfast is consumed, you can remain alert and energized, even though you are eating a carbohydrate based meal exclusively.

It is also important to note that during high carbohydrate meals, fats and oils intake should be relatively LOW (not higher than 20-30%), or you may risk storing those fats as bodyfat due to the presence of insulin. If fat is consumed during a low carbohydrate meal, your body can access and use some of that fat as fuel if needed. This is due to the fact that insulin is in check and your body can burn fat. During a high carbohydrate meal, insulin is released to control the glucose created from the carbohydrate content of the meal and also to help convert the excess glucose (blood sugar) into glycogen (muscle starch stored for later use).

Because insulin stops your body from burning fat, if you consume too much fat at your carb-loading meals, much of that fat may be converted into triglyceride (bodyfat), simply because your body can't burn fat during the times insulin is present and you are replenishing glycogen levels. But because fat SLOWS the digestion of foods, including carbohydrate, some fat is beneficial to create a slower release of sugar into the bloodstream, due to a slowing of the digestion of the carbohydrate consumed. So fats and oils are kept low during the carb-loading phase.

Also, by limiting fats and oils at carb-loading meals, you are insuring that you will not overeat. When butter is applied to warm, fresh bread, the calorie content of that meal may easily DOUBLE, and the taste sensation may drive you to overeat. But, if you will avoid the butter and eat the bread plain, you will enjoy it but not over consume it because your body will not be drawn to that decadent combination of fats and carbs.

With the exception of fresh fruit, Stevia and Agave, should you suddenly realize you are consuming something that tastes SWEET, spit it out! Your carb-loading meals should be a bit bland, thus making them non-addictive. In my opinion, the most addictive and deadly combination of foods in America are the "sugar-fat" combinations. This translates to sweet-treats that are high in fat and high in refined sugar. It is bad enough to consume a high sugar treat, but to also consume that treat if it is high in fat should be illegal...except during your once per week "anything goes" free meal. A typical example of a "deadly carb-fat combination" would be pancakes with butter and syrup, most desserts, candy bars, cakes, pies, cookies, chocolate, French toast with butter and syrup, doughnuts, regular ice cream, milk shakes, and French fries, all of which are avoided on The Fat Burning Diet. But I have good news...

You can have your cake and eat it too on The Fat Burning Diet! With the use of stevia, agave, and fresh fruit, you can "safely" have that sweet sensation without the "high" and without getting fat or fatter. Let's get on with the high-carb breakfast recipes...

"Twins are an infant replay."

Egg Rolls and Toast

Protein: 22g
Fat: 5g
Carbohydrate: 46
Calories: 317

Ingredients:
5 egg whites 1 yolk (scrambled together)
3 slices 100% Flourless, No-salt Sprouted Grain Bread
2 tsp. Sea Seasonings Dulse Flakes with Garlic
Agave

Lightly coat a non-stick skillet with olive oil or an olive oil spray, and cook the scrambled eggs covered, on low to medium heat, until all the whites are solid. Next slide out the cooked egg whites flat onto a large plate. Evenly sprinkle the top of the whites with the dulse and garlic seasoning, then roll-up the eggs whites like a burrito. Toast the sprouted grain bread, lightly top with Agave and enjoy a low-fat, high natural carbohydrate breakfast that is delicious, nutritious and glycogen replenishing.

Carbo-Power Pancakes (serves 3)

Per Serving:
Protein: 17g
Fat: 7g
Carbohydrate: 64
Calories: 389

Ingredients:
Pancakes
3/4 cups rice flour
3/4 cups corn flour
1 tsp. aluminum-free baking powder
1 oz. whey protein powder, egg white protein or soy protein
1 1/2 cups water or non-fat milk
3 egg whites
1 tbs. olive oil
1 tsp. warm Agave

Agave Maple Syrup
 8 oz. bottle of Agave
2 tsp. maple flavoring
(warm the Agave in the microwave for 20 seconds, or place in
a pan of hot water for 3 minutes, then mix the maple flavoring
to form a natural maple flavored syrup)

Begin with two bowls. Mix the dry ingredients in one bowl and
the wet ingredients in another bowl. Next, pour the dry ingredients into the wet ingredients and stir until mixed. To cook, pour
approximately 1/4 cup of the batter into a non-stick medium
heated skillet and cook until brown on the bottom then flip and
brown the other side. When cooked on both sides, transfer each
pancake to a plate and top lightly the Agave-maple syrup.

*"There's a weight loss center on Wall
Street for stocky brokers."*

Apple-Blueberry Pancakes (serves 3)

Per Serving:
Protein: 8g
Fat: 7g
Carbohydrate: 66
Calories: 354

Ingredients:
Pancakes
3/4 cups rice flour
3/4 cups corn flour
1 tsp. aluminum-free baking powder
1 1/2 cups water or non-fat milk
2 egg whites
1 tbs. olive oil
1 tsp. warm Agave
1 cup fresh or frozen blueberries
1 medium apple (peeled and grated)

Begin with two bowls. Mix the dry ingredients in one bowl and
the wet ingredients in another bowl. Next, pour the dry ingredients into the wet ingredients and stir until mixed. Add the
blueberries and grated apple last and stir in until well mixed. To
cook, pour approximately 1/4 cup of the batter into a non-stick
medium heated skillet and cook until brown on the bottom then
flip and brown the other side. When cooked on both sides,
transfer each pancake to a plate, top lightly the Agave or
Agave-maple syrup.

One doctor to another: "With the cost of real estate and my son's tuition, how can they say these are unnecessary operations?"

Killer French Toast

Protein: 26g
Fat: 10g
Carbohydrate: 55g
Calories: 409

Ingredients:
4 slices 100% Flourless, Sprouted Grain, No-Salt Bread
4 egg whites and 1 yolk
2 tsp. cinnamon powder

In a medium size bowl, whip the egg whites and yolk together until well mixed. Lay one slice of bread in the bowl and flip it over so that both sides are covered with the egg batter. Place the coated bread into a non-stick skillet and cook over medium heat until brown on the bottom, then flip over and brown the other side. Remove from skillet and place on a plate, then sprinkle with cinnamon powder. Top with plain Agave syrup, or Agave maple syrup. You will truly enjoy this high natural carb, low calorie breakfast delight.

"I've always called bankruptcy a debt-defying act."

Cottage Cheese Power Pancakes (serves 2)

Per Serving:
Protein: 37g
Fat: 4g
Carbohydrate: 49g
Calories: 492

Ingredients:
1 cup low-fat cottage cheese
1/3 cup non-fat milk
3 egg whites
1/2 cup rice flour
1/2 cup corn flour
1 oz. vanilla whey protein
1 tsp. warm Agave

Combine the eggs, milk and cottage cheese in a blender. Blend until smooth. Add in the flour, whey protein and Agave and blend again. Medium heat a non-stick skillet and cook pancakes until golden brown on both sides. Top with sliced bananas and Agave for a special treat.

"Warranties are the agreements that expire two weeks before your purchase breaks down."

Wheat-Free Wonder-Waffles (serves 2)

Per Serving:
Protein: 16g
Fat: 10g
Carbohydrate: 36g
Calories: 496

Ingredients:
1/4 cup raw almonds
3/4 cup very warm water
1 tbs. Agave
1 tbs. olive oil
3 egg whites
1 cup cooked brown rice
2/3 cup brown or white rice flour
1/3 cup potato flour
3/4 tsp. baking soda

Grind the nuts until very fine in the blender then add the water and blend further until well mixed. Next, add the egg whites and buzz briefly until well mixed.

In a large bowl, mix the dry ingredients then pour in the liquid ingredients and stir until well mixed.

Bake according to directions listed with your waffle iron.

*"A secret is something I tell to
only one person at a time."*

Cream of Rice (serves 2)

Per Serving:
Protein: 8g
Fat: 5g
Carbohydrate: 80g
Calories: 390

Ingredients:
1 cup finely cracked rice (whole grain rice chopped in a blender
or purchased this way)
3 cups water
1 tsp. olive oil
1 tsp. cinnamon
1 tbs. Agave syrup

Bring the water to a boil, then add the rice, reduce heat and
cook for 7-10 minutes until creamy smooth. Top with olive oil,
cinnamon and Agave. This is a great carb-loading breakfast that
is non-allergenic and delicious. I often mix one ounce of our
delicious whey protein in 6 ounces of water as a quick protein
drink that I consume prior to eating this high-carb cereal, or
sometimes I pour it over the top of the cereal like milk.

"It's obvious to me that most
bodybuilders are biceptual."

Eggs and Hash Browns

Protein: 22g
Fat: 5g
Carbohydrate: 53g
Calories: 346

Ingredients:
4 egg whites and 1 yolk
1 large Russet potato (washed and grated)

Heat two non-stick skillets, one on medium-high and the other on medium-low. Spray both with a non-stick cooking spray (or lightly coat with olive oil) and place the eggs in the low-medium heated skillet and the grated potato in the medium-high heated skillet. Spread the grated potato evenly in the pan. Cover the skillet with the eggs and reduce the heat to low. Cook the eggs until the whites are solid and the yolk is white on top but still runny, then slide out onto a plate. Cook the potato until golden brown on one side, flip it over and brown the other side, then slide onto a plate. May be served with a few slices of 100% flourless, no-salt, sprouted grain bread. The toast may be lightly buttered or covered with a natural nut butter.

*"It is only possible to live happily ever
after on a day-to-day basis."*

Melon Mania

Protein: 5g
Fat: 2g
Carbohydrate: 81g
Calories: 323

Ingredients:
1/2 medium size honeydew
1/2 medium size cantaloupe
1/4 medium size seedless watermelon

Remove seeds from the cantaloupe and honeydew, then with a melon ball utensil or regular spoon, scoop out all the flesh of each melon into a bowl, mix lightly and enjoy this tasty melon delight. This breakfast is great during the warm summer months and will kick you off to a cool start.

"I firmly believe that contraceptives should be used on every conceivable occasion."

Quick Apple Pancakes

Protein: 15g
Fat: 9g
Carbohydrate: 95g
Calories: 540

Ingredients:
1 cup of Arrowhead Mills Wild Rice Pancake Mix (gluten free)
2 egg whites
1 cup water
1 tbs. olive oil
1 apple (grated)

Mix all wet ingredients in a bowl (except the grated apple) then add the pancake mix and stir with a fork until blended. Add the grated apple and mix lightly. Pour 1/4 cup batter into a non-stick pan heated to medium-high and cook until golden brown then flip over to brown the second side. Slide onto a plate, top with Agave and enjoy!

*"Experience is what you get when you
didn't get what you wanted."*

Huevos and Tortillas

Protein: 19g
Fat: 7g
Carbohydrate: 45g
Calories: 315

Ingredients:
3 egg whites and one yolk
3 corn tortillas
2 tbs. fresh salsa

Place the eggs in a bowl and mix thoroughly with a fork until well beaten. Pour the eggs in a non-stick pan and cook as scrambled eggs, turning them frequently until firm. Place one tortilla in another non-stick skillet heated on medium-high, cover and cook until warm and steamy, then flip over and heat the second side until the tortilla is piping hot. Place the hot tortilla on a plate and cover with 1/3 of the scrambled eggs, top with salsa, then roll-up the tortilla and enjoy.

*"It seems to me that computer chips are
small because computers take small bytes."*

Skillet Spuds

Protein: 4g
Fat: 5g
Carbohydrate: 34
Calories: 185

Ingredients:
1 large Russet potato
1 tsp. olive oil

Thoroughly wash the potato then cut into half-inch squares.
Place the olive oil in a non-stick skillet heated to medium-high
and spread the oil evenly with a paper towel. Next, add the
potato pieces and cook until all sides are browned by stirring
frequently. Serve on the side with eggs cooked your favorite
way, a cooked chicken breast or a broiled hamburger patty.

"The other day I asked my wife what was for dinner and she said, "Take-out." I said, "What kind of take-out?" And she said, "Me."

Agave Cinnamon Toast

Protein: 4g
Fat: 1g
Carbohydrate: 37g
Calories: 147

Ingredients:
2 slices 100% Flourless Sprouted Grain Bread
1 tbs. Agave
1 tsp. cinnamon

Toast both slices of bread and top with Agave and cinnamon, then cut each slice of toast in half and enjoy! Goes great with two or three scrambled egg whites.

*"I was devastated to discover last week that, The
Three Little Pigs once did time in the pen."*

Cilantro Rice and Eggs

Protein: 18g
Fat: 7g
Carbohydrate: 72g
Calories: 393

Ingredients:
1 cup cooked brown rice
3 egg whites
1 tsp. flax seed oil
2 tbs. fresh cilantro leaves

In a pan heat 1 cup pure water to a boil then add 1/2 cup brown
rice, let the water return to a boil then reduce the heat and cook
for 35-40 minutes until the rice is soft and tender. (This makes
about 2 cups of cooked rice. You can save the extra for another
meal.) In a non-stick skillet lightly coated with olive oil and
heated to medium-low, pour in the eggs and cook by scrambling
with a spatula until solid. Pour the rice onto a plate, top with
the scrambled eggs and toss together lightly. Sprinkle with
cilantro and dribble the top with the flax seed oil.

*"I have noticed in southern California, it's
not easy to tell a real cliff from a bluff."*

Power Potatoes

Protein: 38g
Fat: 17g
Carbohydrate: 38g
Calories: 467

Ingredients:
1 Russet potato (washed and cut into 1/2 inch cubes)
4 oz. lean ground sirloin
1/2 of a white onion (chopped)
2 tsp. olive oil

Begin by heating 2 skillets, coated with olive oil, on medium
heat. In one skillet place the onion and top with the sirloin
evenly filling the skillet by pinching off small pieces of the meat.
Cook until meat is browned. In the other skillet, place the
potato pieces and stir regularly until all sides are brown. Next,
place the meat into the pan with the cooked potatoes and stir
together lightly then slide onto a plate. This dish is great as is or
may be topped with salsa, guacamole, and a few leaves of
cilantro.

"For my first real job I was hired as an accountant for a traveling circus, but got caught 'juggling' the books."

Fast Eggs and Waffles

Protein: 27g
Fat: 16g
Carbohydrate: 56g
Calories: 475

Ingredients:
3 egg whites, one yolk (whipped together in a bowl)
1 oz. non-fat or low-fat grated cheese (optional)
2 wheat-free, gluten-free toaster waffles (frozen from health food store)
2 tsp. Agave

Heat a non-stick skillet on low-medium, coat lightly with olive oil and pour in the eggs. Cook, stirring lightly until solid, then slide onto a plate and top with the grated cheese. Place the waffles in a toaster and toast until golden brown, place on a plate and dribble with Agave. Eat the eggs and cheese first and the waffles last to insure you block the insulin-Tryptophan-serotonin response.

*"When it comes to giving, some
people stop at nothing."*

Power Apple Sauce

Protein: 2g
Fat: 2g
Carbohydrate: 104g
Calories: 403

Ingredients:
3 large apples (cored, peeled and cut into sections)

Place apples in a blender and blend on low-medium until creamy smooth. Add small amounts of water if needed to make the apples into a sauce while blending. Pour into a bowl and enjoy. This is a great meal for anyone, and small children especially love this morning treat.

When my son Angelo was a baby, he was fed breast milk only until he was around five months old, at which time we also introduced our Power Applesauce into his diet. We used organic apples and he ate this every day for several years along with breast milk. We gradually introduced other fresh fruits into his diet and avoided grains and cereals until he was around 13 months old and could digest then properly (most infants do not secrete the proper enzymes to digest starches until after their first birthday). At 13 months we gradually introduced, other fresh fruits, lean meats, Jay Robb's Protein Powders, rice, potatoes, squash, veggies and other whole foods. Milk was avoided also, except for breast milk.

Angelo was not sick for his first five years of life (not even a sniffle!), and when he finally did get sick it was just a slight cold which he contracted after being flexible with his diet for several days. We attribute his outstanding state of health to an immune system that was boosted daily with plenty of breast milk, Power Applesauce, and a natural food diet void of wheat, most grains, sugar, junk food, processed food and milk.

*"After 12 years of therapy, my psychiatrist
said something that brought tears to my
eyes. He said, 'No hablo ingles'."*
—Ronnie Shakes

Chapter 6

What's For Lunch?

Low-Carb Lunches

Chicken Salad Supreme

Protein: 30g
Fat: 10g
Carbohydrate: 9g
Calories: 245

Ingredients:
1 large boneless, skinless chicken breast
2 cups romaine lettuce (cleaned and cut into small 1 inch pieces)
4 cherry tomatoes (washed and cut in half)
1/8 small head of red cabbage (chopped)
1 tbs. of your favorite dressing

Grill the chicken breast on an outdoor barbecue or indoor grilling machine until cooked. This usually requires about 7-8 minutes, turning once, to grill both sides unless you have a two sided grilling machine. Cut the chicken into small pieces. Place all salad ingredients in a large bowl, add the chicken and top with your favorite dressing and dig in! This is one of my favorite lunches on low-carb days!

*"Maintenance-free" means that when
it breaks, it can't be fixed.*

Almost Pizza

Protein: 52g
Fat: 32g
Carbohydrate: 16g
Calories: 561

Ingredients:
4 oz. ground sirloin (7% lean)
1/2 large red onion (peeled and chopped)
1 large zucchini (washed, ends cut off, and thin sliced)
3 tbs. low-fat, low-sodium, pasta sauce
2 oz. low-fat mozzarella cheese (grated)
2 black olives
1 tsp. olive oil

In a non-stick skillet coated with the olive oil, place the onion
and ground sirloin and cook on medium-high until meat is
browned. Place the zucchini on a plate and microwave for 2-3
minutes until soft (or steam in a pan until soft). Top the zucchini
with the cooked meat, pasta sauce, cheese and olives, then grab
your fork and dig in! Tastes just like your favorite pizza but
without the high-carb crust.

"A flood occurs when a river gets too big for its bridges."

Spicy Turkey Topped Zucchini

Protein: 36g
Fat: 3g
Carbohydrate: 11g
Calories: 206

Ingredients:
5 oz. low-salt, sliced turkey breast (chopped)
2 medium zucchini (washed and sliced)
2 tbs. fresh salsa
1/4 wedge of lime

Steam the zucchini until soft to the touch, then place on a large plate. Top with fresh salsa and turkey...then squeeze the lime juice over the top. This is a filling lunch that is easy-to-make and pleasant to the palate. This is a low-calorie lunch that can be boosted with a large green salad and/or a small protein drink if desired.

*"My wife confessed to me the other day
that her favorite labor saving device is
a husband with money."*

Green Beans, Basil and Beef

Protein: 60g
Fat: 16g
Carbohydrate: 34
Calories: 492

Ingredients:
6 oz. 7% lean ground sirloin
1 tsp. olive oil
1/2 small red onion (chopped)
1.5 cups green beans
2 tbs. low-salt, low-fat pasta sauce
1 green onion (washed and chopped)
3 large fresh basil leaves (minced)

In a medium heated non-stick skillet, place the olive oil (rubbed around the skillet with a paper towel) onion and sirloin (placed on top of the onions by pinching off small bits until the onions are evenly covered). Cook until the meat is browned and then remove from heat. In a saucepan, steam the green beans until tender (frozen beans may require 10-12 minutes, fresh may require 10-15 minutes). Place the green beans on a plate and top with the cooked sirloin. Top this with the pasta sauce, green onion and fresh basil. Mmmm Good! This is a fast and fine tasting low-carb lunch you will want to have again and again.

Years ago I discovered a sure-fire way to
get the last word in everytime my wife
and I argue, no matter how heated the
argument. I simply say, "I agree."

Tuna in the Cabbage Patch

Protein: 38g
Fat: 12g
Carbohydrate: 14g
Calories: 312

Ingredients:
1 can spring water packed Albacore, no-salt tuna (drained and chopped)
1 tsp. flax seed oil
1/4 medium head of cabbage (sliced thin or shredded)
1 tbs. no-salt mustard
3 raw walnuts (chopped)
3 grapes (chopped)
1 celery stalk (chopped very thin)

Place tuna, flax oil, mustard, grapes and celery in a bowl and mix well. Spread the shredded cabbage onto a large dinner plate and top with the tuna mixture and sprinkle with the chopped walnuts. This is a very powerful lunch that is low in carbs, rich in protein, and loaded with essential fatty acids, especially Omega-3 oils.

When I was a little boy, my Grandmother lived on a small farm with a few chickens that produced a lot of eggs. One day I asked my Grandmother why her chickens were so productive. She took me to the chicken coop and pointed to a sign that read, "An egg a day keeps Colonel Sanders away."

Jay's Big-Bad-Burger

Protein: 68g
Fat: 37g
Carbohydrate: 15g
Calories: 665

Ingredients:
8 oz. 7% lean ground sirloin
1/2 small white onion (chopped)
1 tsp. olive oil
1/4 red pepper (chopped fine)
1/4 Haas avocado (peeled and chopped)
1 tbs. fresh salsa

In a bowl place the meat, 1/2 of the onion, olive oil, and 1/2 the red pepper and mix with your hands until well combined. Next, form the meat mixture into a large patty and cook in a non-stick skillet until both sides are browned and the center is light pink or light brown. Slide the patty onto a plate and top with the remaining onion, pepper, avocado, and fresh salsa. This powerful burger goes great with a green vegetable salad and your favorite low-fat dressing.

"Have you ever noticed some people are like blisters;
they always show up after the work is finished."

Avo-Almond Green Beans and Chicken

Protein: 40g
Fat: 32g
Carbohydrate: 16g
Calories: 484

Ingredients:
1 cup fresh or frozen green beans
10 raw almonds (chopped lightly in a blender)
1 chicken breast (grilled, and cut into small pieces)
1/2 small ripe Haas avocado (peeled, pitted and cut into small
cubes)

Steam the green beans until tender. This usually requires 8-12
minutes or more. Grill the chicken breast on an outdoor or
indoor grill for 6-10 minutes until cooked but not dry. Coat the
breast lightly with olive oil to keep it moist while cooking and
after taking it off the grill, then cut it into small pieces. Place the
cooked green beans on a large plate, top with the chicken
pieces, avocado cubes and sprinkle with the chopped almonds.
This is a fantastic, low-carb, very satisfying and highly nutritious lunch that can easily be prepared in 20 minutes. This lunch
also is great to make in advance then place in a microwave
container to heat up for lunch at work or when you are on the
go. When making this delightful dish in advance, set the avocado and almonds aside and add them after the chicken and
green beans are reheated.

"Last year Jay's Gym started a lunch hour workout program for corporate executives who's waistlines had expanded. We called the group, 'Middle Management'."

Terrific Tuna Salad

Protein: 38g
Fat: 5g
Carbohydrate: 8g
Calories: 229

Ingredients:
1 - 6 oz. can of no salt tuna in spring water (check that the label states tuna and water only).
1 tbs. stone ground no salt mustard
1/4 small white onion (chopped)
1/2 ripe Haas avocado (peeled, pit removed)
2 cups Romaine lettuce (washed and cut into 1 inch pieces)

Place all ingredients in a bowl and mix together by first mashing the avocado then stirring until all ingredients are well blended. Place the cut-up lettuce in a bowl and top with the tuna mix. For an extra treat, toss in few ripe cherry tomatoes and dig in!

I'll never forget my very first speech. I started out addressing a full auditorium and one by one, everyone left during my speech except for one man on the front row. After I finished, I walked down and asked him why he stayed. The man said, "I'm the next speaker."

Tuna and Egg-Salad

Protein: 58g
Fat: 16g
Carbohydrate: 11g
Calories: 424

Ingredients:
1 - 6 oz. can of water packed, no salt tuna (label must state, tuna and water only)
1 tbs. Omega-3 Mayonnaise (see recipe in Chapter 12)
2 hard boiled eggs (peeled, one yolk discarded and sliced)
1 tsp. mustard
1 green onion (chopped)

In a bowl place all the ingredients and mix well. This taste treat is great by itself or can be placed over a salad or steamed vegetables for a delicious and nutritious low-carb lunch.

*"A friend of mine once told me the
most difficult years of marriage are
those following the wedding."*

Spicy Ground Sirloin and Onions

Protein: 67g
Fat: 27g
Carbohydrate: 14g
Calories: 467

Ingredients:
8 oz. 7% lean ground sirloin
1/2 medium red onion (chopped)
1 tsp. extra virgin olive oil
1 zucchini (washed, ends cut off and sliced)
1/2 ripe Haas avocado (peeled, pitted and cubed)
2 tbs. Salsa Fresca (see Chapter 12 for recipe)

Coat a non-stick skillet with the olive oil, then add the onion
and sirloin, tearing off bits of sirloin at a time until the onions
are evenly coated. Cook on medium-high heat until the meat is
cooked and evenly brown. In a separate pan, steam the zucchini
or place it in the microwave for 2 1/2 to 3 minutes, until soft
and tender. Spread the zucchini evenly on a large plate and top
with the cooked sirloin, salsa and avocado. This is one of my
favorite lunches that I eat at least 4-5 times a week. When I am
training hard, it is not unusual for me to consume, each day, a
pound of 7% ground sirloin. Red meat is loaded with B-vita-
mins, iron and creatine.

*"The only reason some people get lost in
thought is because it's unfamiliar territory."*
—Paul Fix

High-Carb Lunches

Grilled Cheese Sandwich

Protein: 18g
Fat: 10g
Carbohydrate: 32g
Calories: 271

Ingredients:
2 slices 100% flourless, no-salt, sprouted grain bread
2 oz. slice low-fat cheddar cheese
1 tsp. olive oil or real butter

Coat one side of the two bread slices with olive oil or butter, then place one slice (oil side down) in a medium-heated, non-stick skillet. Top the slice of bread with the cheese and place the other slice of bread over the cheese, oil side up. Brown the bread then turn-over and brown the other side, then place on a plate, slice in half and enjoy this low-fat, moderate protein, high carbohydrate delight!

In front of our offices, I overheard one of our less enthusiastic employees talking to a friend who asked, "How long have you been working here?" And our employee quickly replied, "Only since my boss threatened to fire me!"

Quick Tuna and Noodles (serves 2)

Per Serving:
Protein: 33g
Fat: 3g
Carbohydrate: 59g
Calories: 406

Ingredients:
2 cups cooked rice-or-corn elbow macaroni
1 can water packed, no-salt Albacore tuna (drained and chopped)
2 oz. low-fat cheddar or low-fat Swiss cheese (grated)

Cook the macaroni according to the package instructions, drain and place on a plate. Top with the tuna and cheese and dig-in! For melted cheese, warm in an oven heated to 375 for a few minutes or place in a microwave for a few seconds.

"Only in America will you find creative companies that own 15 Doughnut Shops and 3 Weight Loss Clinics."

Peanut Butter and Agave Sandwich

Protein: 12g
Fat: 17g
Carbohydrate: 42
Calories: 336

Ingredients:
2 slices 100% flourless, no-salt, sprouted grain bread
2 tbs. natural peanut butter (no salt, no sugar, no preservatives)
1-2 tsp. Agave

Spread each slice of bread with peanut butter, then dribble each with Agave. Place the two slices together, cut in half and enjoy. The Agave adds a safe sweetness to the sandwich and lets you avoid the sugars and simple carbs found in honey or jelly. This sandwich is also great when toasted.

*A good friend of mine once confessed to
me that his father was a great Western
politician in his day. So I said, "What did
he run for?" My friend said, "The border."*

Bountiful Baked Potato

Protein: 19g
Fat: 7g
Carbohydrate: 45g
Calories: 310

Ingredients:
1 large Russet potato (washed)
2 fresh mushrooms (washed and sliced)
1 oz. low-fat cheese (grated)
2 egg whites (scrambled)
1 tbs. fresh salsa
1 green onion (chopped)
1 tbs. non-fat plain yogurt
1 tsp. olive oil

Coat the potato with olive oil, wrap in aluminum foil and bake
at 375 degrees Fahrenheit for 60-90 minutes until soft. Unwrap
the potato, cut it in half and place it on a large plate with the
middle facing up. Lightly mash the white portion of the potato
with a fork, then top with cheese, egg whites, mushrooms,
salsa, onion and top with yogurt. This is a hearty lunch that is
easy to make and very satisfying.

In comparing our likes and dislikes,
last week my wife asked me if I like
Kipling? To this I replied, "I don't
know, I have never kippled."

Mint Millet and Tuna

Protein: 58g
Fat: 12g
Carbohydrate: 48g
Calories: 537

Ingredients:
1/2 cup millet (rinsed four times with water)
1 1/2 cups pure water
1 can no-salt Albacore tuna in spring water (chopped)
2 sprigs fresh spearmint (washed, chopped)
1 cup frozen peas (cooked according to package directions)
2 tsp. flax seed oil

Heat the water in a pan to boiling, add the millet, return to a boil, reduce heat and cook for 15-20 minutes until most of the water is absorbed, then remove from heat. Next, put the millet on a large plate, top (in the following order) with the cooked peas, tuna, spearmint and top with flax oil. This is an easy and fast lunch that will help you reload glycogen and keep you burning fat.

"Where do you go to get anorexia?"
—Shelly Winters

Quick Turkey Melt
Protein: 21g
Fat: 6g
Carbohydrate: 32g
Calories: 253

Ingredients:
2 slices 100% flourless, sprouted, no salt, whole grain bread
2 oz. low-sodium turkey breast (sliced thin)
1 oz. non-fat or very low-fat cheese (3 grams fat or less per ounce)
1 tsp. olive oil

Heat a non-stick skillet on medium, then coat one side of one slice of bread with olive oil and place olive oil side down in the skillet. Place the turkey and cheese on the bread and cover with the remaining slice of bread. Coat the top slice of bread with olive oil and cook until bread is light brown, then flip over, cover the skillet with a lid and brown the other slice. Because the skillet is covered, the cheese will melt slightly and the turkey will be piping hot. Place the toasted sandwich on a plate, cut in half and enjoy!

*"Talk is cheap because supply always
exceeds the demand."*

Turkey Tacos

Protein: 24g
Fat: 5g
Carbohydrate: 38g
Calories: 282

Ingredients:
2 soft corn tortillas
2 oz. low-salt, cooked and sliced turkey breast (chopped and warmed)
1 oz. non-fat or low-fat cheese (grated)
2 tbs. fresh salsa
2 tbs. fresh cilantro leaves (stems removed and washed)
1/4 white onion (peeled and chopped)
1/2 of a fresh lime

Heat a non-stick skillet to medium-high heat and place one tortilla flat in the skillet, cover and heat until very lightly browned, then flip over the tortilla and heat the other side to light brown also. Place the piping hot tortilla on a plate and cover with 1/2 of: the turkey, cheese, salsa, onion, cilantro and dribble with fresh lime juice. Next, roll up the tortilla to house the ingredients in the middle and enjoy a delicious soft-rolled Turkey Taco.

"Kites rise highest against the wind—not with it."
—Winston Churchill

Turkey Power-Pasta

Protein: 30g
Fat: 9g
Carbohydrate: 57g
Calories: 425

Ingredients:
1 cup Gluten-Free pasta of choice (cooked according to label directions)
2 oz. low-salt, cooked and sliced turkey breast (chopped)
3 oz. low-salt, low-fat, sugar-free pasta sauce (warmed)
1 oz. non-fat or low-fat cheese (grated)

Place the cooked, drained and piping hot pasta on a large plate, top with the turkey, pasta sauce and cheese. Now dig in! This dish is fast, easy and delicious! This meal goes great with a medium size tossed vegetable salad topped with 1 tsp. flax seed oil and lemon juice.

Squashed Rice

Protein: 37g
Fat: 13g
Carbohydrate: 52g
Calories: 466

Ingredients:
1/4 butternut squash
1/2 cup long-grain brown rice (cooked)
1 chicken breast (cooked and chopped)
1/4 cup frozen peas (cooked according to package directions)
2 tbs. fresh cilantro leaves (washed and stems removed)
1 tsp. flax seed oil

Prepare squash and rice in advance. Half a butternut squash, scoop out the seeds and lay flat (skin side up) on a large baking pan that contains a half inch lip around the edges. Fill the shallow pan with water and bake on 350-375 degrees Fahrenheit for 60-90 minutes until the squash is very soft. Set aside to cool. To prepare rice, boil 2 cups pure water, then add in 1 cup of rice, return to boiling then reduce heat and cook for 30-40 more minutes until the water is mostly absorbed and the rice is light and tender. Remove from heat and allow to cool. Now it is time to build your squash and rice masterpiece! On a large plate place 1/2 cup of the cooked rice. Top this with 1/4 of the butternut squash scooping out a spoonful at a time until the rice is evenly covered. Now top this with the chopped chicken breast, peas, cilantro leaves and dribble it all with flax seed oil. This is a great meal that offers a natural sweet taste from the peas and squash, contains plenty of protein and also offers a bountiful amount of the essential fatty acids. Enjoy!

*"Stop thinking so much and take action in
the direction your heart desires."*

Yam-n-Sandwich

Protein: 28g
Fat: 11g
Carbohydrate: 46g
Calories: 388

Ingredients:
1 large yam
1 slice 100% flourless, no-salt, sprouted grain bread
2 oz. thin sliced, low-salt, cooked turkey breast
1 tsp. no-sugar, natural mayonnaise
2 thin slices of a white onion
1 oz. thin slice of very low-fat or non-fat cheese
1 1/2 tsp. olive oil or butter

Coat the yam with olive oil or butter, pierce the skin with a
fork, wrap in aluminum foil and bake at 350 degrees Fahrenheit
for 60-90 minutes until soft to the touch. Set aside to cool
slightly. To prepare the sandwich, coat one side with olive oil or
butter and one side with the mayonnaise and place the slice of
bread, oil side down in a skillet heated to medium. Place the
turkey on top of the mayonnaise side of the bread, then the
onion and top with the cheese. Cover the skillet and cook until
the bread is lightly browned and the cheese is slightly melted.
Place the open-face sandwich and yam on a large plate and
enjoy. Goes great with celery and carrot sticks!

*"It just doesn't seem right to go over the
river and through the woods to
Grandmother's condo."*

Pizza Quick

Protein: 22g
Fat: 15g
Carbohydrate: 38g
Calories: 366

Ingredients:
2 slices 100% flourless, no-salt, sprouted grain bread
4 tbs. low-fat, low-sodium pasta sauce
2 oz. low-fat mozzarella cheese (sliced or shredded)

Lightly toast the bread in a toaster then place both slices on a
plate and evenly top with pasta sauce and cheese. Place both
slices in a toaster oven and top broil until the cheese melts
slightly. Remove from the toaster oven and it's pizza time!

"After two decades of counseling individuals on diet and weight loss, some people are simply no good at counting carbohydrates— and they have the figures to prove it."

Chapter 7

What's For Dinner?

Low-Carb Dinners

This Chapter will begin with some basic recipes for protein foods which are the staples for low-carb meals.

Baked Chicken Breasts

Protein: 53g
Fat: 15g
Carbohydrate: 0g
Calories: 362

Ingredients:
2 boneless, skinless chicken breasts
2 tsp. olive oil or butter

Place chicken breasts in a lightly oiled roasting pan and cover the breasts with oil or butter, cover the pan and bake at 400 degrees for 25-40 minutes until the meat is very juicy and tender.

*"In any moment of decision, the best thing
you can do is the right thing; the next best
thing is the wrong thing; and the worst
thing you can do is nothing."*
—*Theodore Roosevelt*

Grilled Chicken Breasts

Protein: 107
Fat: 25.8
Carbohydrate: 0
Calories: 683

Ingredients:
4 boneless, skinless chicken breasts
1 tbs. olive oil or butter

Lightly coat the chicken with the oil or butter and place the breasts on a barbecue grill or indoor grill. Cook lightly on both sides until the meat is tender and not dry, yet thoroughly cooked. Cooking time varies from 6 to 12 minutes depending on the size of the chicken breasts and the cooking temperature.

*"My hyusband lost a lot of weight on a
new diet, and I resent it. It's simple, he
just doesn't eat when I'm talking."*
—Wendy Morgan

Broiled Fish

Protein: 135g
Fat: 44g
Carbohydrate: 0
Calories: 967

Ingredients:
1 lb. fresh fish fillets of choice
1 tbs. olive oil or butter

Place the fish in an aluminum foil lined broiling pan and lightly coat the top side of the fish with the oil or butter. Broil for 6 to 12 minutes until the fish is lightly browned on top and the meat is flaky and tender, but not dry.

"If your ship doesn't come in, swim out to it."
—*Jonathan Winters*

Rosemary Almond Chicken

Protein: 34g
Fat: 22g
Carbohydrate: 14g
Calories: 379

Ingredients:
1 large chicken breast (cooked as shown earlier in this chapter and cut into small pieces)
1 cup frozen green beans (cooked according to package directions)
10 raw almonds (chopped in a blender)
1 tsp. real butter
1/2 tsp. dried Rosemary
1 sprig of fresh Rosemary

Place the green beans on a large plate and rub them with the butter until evenly coated. Top the beans with the chicken, dried Rosemary, sprinkle with the chopped almonds and top it all with the sprig of fresh Rosemary. The aroma of the fresh Rosemary is heavenly and, even though it is not eaten with the meal, will add to the aromatic taste delight of this outstanding meal.

*"The trouble with most of us is that we would rather
be ruined by praise than saved by criticism."*
—Norman Vincent Peale

Fat Burning Tacos

Protein: 59g
Fat: 34g
Carbohydrate: 19g
Calories: 646

Ingredients:
6 oz. 7% lean ground sirloin
1 small white onion (chopped)
4 whole Romaine lettuce leaves (washed)
1 tsp. olive oil
1 oz. low fat cheese (grated)
1/4 Haas avocado (pit removed and cubed)
2 tbs. Salsa Fresca (see recipe in Chapter 13)

Place the olive oil, half the onion, and the sirloin in a non-stick skillet and cook on medium high until browned. Then, one at a time, fill a Romaine lettuce leaf with meat (like you would a taco shell), sprinkle with onion, cheese and top with avocado and salsa. This is a delicious, low-carb alternative to the traditional high fat and high carb taco.

*"Right now I have enough money to last me
the rest of my life—unless I buy something."*
—*Jackie Mason*

Grilled Chicken Salad

Protein: 39g
Fat: 32g
Carbohydrate: 7g
Calories: 470

Ingredients:
1 large chicken breast (grilled and sliced into strips)
2 cups Romaine lettuce (washed and cut into small salad pieces)
1 cucumber (peeled and sliced)
1 oz. low fat mozzarella cheese (grated)
2 tsp. Balsamic vinegar
1 tbs. olive oil or flax seed oil
3 cherry tomatoes (washed)

In a large salad bowl, place the lettuce and cucumber, top with
the chicken slices and sprinkle with the cheese. Next, dribble the
salad with the Balsamic vinegar, oil of choice and toss in the 3
cherry tomatoes. This is a filling and delicious salad that is easy
to make and very satisfying to your taste buds.

Rosemary's Low-Carb Stuffed Peppers (serves 2)

Per serving:
Protein: 54g
Fat: 24g
Carbohydrate: 15g
Calories: 501

Ingredients:
12 oz. 7% lean ground sirloin
1 stalk celery (washed and chopped)
1 tsp. olive oil
1 small white onion (chopped)
2 large green bell peppers (cut in half, seeds removed and steamed until tender)
1 oz. low fat cheese (grated)
1 tbs. low fat sour cream
1 tbs. dried basil
1 tbs. parsley
1 tsp. dried Rosemary
2 sprigs fresh Rosemary
1 clove fresh garlic
1 large tomato (washed and sliced)

Place onions, meat, celery, Rosemary, basil, olive oil and parsley in a non-stick skillet and cook on medium-high until the meat is lightly browned then remove from heat and set aside. Place the steamed pepper halves in a non-stick baking pan and fill each (evenly divided) with the cooked meat, top with the grated cheese and bake at 325 degrees for 12-15 minutes until warm and the cheese melts. Remove from oven, and top with a dollop of low fat sour cream on each. Serve on a plate and place the tomato slices in a row next to the peppers, and topped with a sprig of fresh Rosemary, for a complimentary color accent.

*"During my 15 years as a personal trainer
and gym owner, all my new clients started out
weighing the same—a hundred and plenty."*

High-Carb Dinners

Many high-carb dinners are made with whole grains, potatoes, yams and winter squash as the feature of the meal. This section will begin with basic cooking directions for these high-carb staples. Wheat, oats, and barley contain gluten and are primarily avoided due to their potentially allergenic properties.

Bountiful Brown Rice

Protein: 15g
Fat: 14g
Carbohydrate: 142g
Calories: 854

Ingredients:
1 cup brown rice
2 cups pure water
2 tsp. olive oil or real butter (not margarine)

Place water, oil and rice in a large saucepan and bring to a rapid boil, then reduce to low heat, cover and cook for 35-45 minutes until the rice is "fluffy" and thoroughly cooked.

"For fast-acting relief, try slowing down."
—Lily Tomlin

Marvelous Millet

Protein: 8g
Fat: 12g
Carbohydrate: 57g
Calories: 364

Ingredients:
1 cup millet (rinsed 4-5 times in cool water)
3 cups pure water
2 tsp. olive oil or real butter (not margarine)

Place water, oil or butter, and millet in a large saucepan and bring to a rapid boil, then reduce heat, cover and cook for 15-20 minutes until the millet is fluffy and pops open.

*"You know you're putting on weight
when you get up from a metal chair
and you have to fluff it up."*

Jay's Big-Bad-Butter-Baked Potatoes

Protein: 12g
Fat: 12g
Carbohydrate: 134g
Calories: 682

Ingredients:
4 large Russet baking potatoes (washed but not peeled)
1 tbs. real butter (not margarine)
4 pieces of aluminum foil (large enough to wrap each potato)

Lightly coat each potato with butter, pierce each potato with a fork to break the skin (this keeps them from exploding) and wrap each with aluminum foil. Bake in a 375 degree preheated oven for an hour (or longer) until each potato is soft to the touch and well cooked. Large potatoes may require up to 1 1/2 hours cooking time. The butter and aluminum foil seal in the moisture and make the skin (where a great deal of nutrients are housed) soft and tender so you can eat the potato...skin and all.

*"You cannot become who you want to be
unless you know who you are now."*

Yams and Sweet Potatoes

Protein: 4g
Fat: 12g
Carbohydrate: 63g
Calories: 369

Ingredients:
4 large yams or sweet potatoes
1 tbs. real butter
4 pieces of aluminum foil

Cook the same as Big-Bad-Butter-Baked Potatoes. For a
special treat, cut the yams in half and top with Agave and 1/2
tsp. of cinnamon.

"Diets are for people who are thick and tired of it."
—*Jacob Braude*

Natural Baked Potato Chips

Protein: 9g
Fat: 9g
Carbohydrate: 102g
Calories: 520

Ingredients:
2 large Russett Potatoes (washed but not peeled)
2 tsp. extra virgin olive oil

Using a very sharp knife, cut each potato into very thin slices, the thinner the better. Spray a baking pan lightly with olive oil (use your air pump oil sprayer) and spread the potato slices evenly across the pan. Spray the potatoes lightly with the olive oil and bake in a 400 degree, preheated oven for 20 to 40 minutes (depending on the thickness of the potato slices) until the chips are lightly browned and crisp. Turn the chips several times while baking so that all sides get crispy. This is a family favorite that is the perfect alternative to the high fat, heavily salted traditional potato chip. For a sweet and delicious variety, use a yam or sweet potato.

"It's more difficult to lose weight without exercise. But I have a philosophy about exercise. I don't think you should punish your legs for something your mouth did. Drag your lips around the block once or twice!"
—Gary Owen

Baked Squash

Protein: 4g
Fat: 2g
Carbohydrate: 117g
Calories: 502

Ingredients:
1 butternut squash (or variety of choice)
1 cup pure water

Cut the squash in half and scoop out the seeds. Place each half face down on a baking pan that is covered with aluminum foil and misted with olive oil. Place the pan in a 375 degree pre-heated oven and fill the pan with water and bake for 40 to 70 minutes depending on the size of your squash. The squash is cooked when it is very soft to the touch.

"A successful person simply sees an opportunity and acts immediately, without hesitation."

Jay's Famous Soft-Rolled Tacos

Protein: 42g
Fat: 31g
Carbohydrate: 63g
Calories: 699

Ingredients:
4 soft, corn tortillas
4 oz. lean ground beef
1 small white onion (chopped)
1/2 Haas avocado (pitted, cubed)
1/2 cup fresh salsa
1/4 cup fresh cilantro leaves (washed, stems removed)
1 lime (quartered)
1 tsp. olive oil
1 tsp. chili powder
1/2 tsp. ground cinnamon

In a non-stick skillet, cook the ground beef and 1/2 the onions until lightly browned, then remove from heat and add the cinnamon and chili powder, stir together and cover. In separate bowls, place the lime quarters, salsa, the remaining onion, cilantro leaves, and avocado. In a small, non-stick skillet, heat the tortillas on medium high until both sides are piping hot then place on a plate and fill with meat, salsa, onions, cilantro, avocado and top with a squeeze of fresh lime. Roll-up each tortilla and enjoy the most awesome soft tacos on the planet.

*"My doctor said I look like a million
dollars—green and wrinkled."*
—Red Skelton

Tofu for You

Protein: 27g
Fat: 23g
Carbohydrate: 80g
Calories: 611

Ingredients:
8 oz. soft tofu (cut into 1/2 inch cubes)
1.5 cups cooked brown rice (see instructions at the beginning of
this chapter)
1/2 cup green peas (cooked according to package directions)
1 tsp. Bragg Liquid Aminos (healthy alternative to traditional
soy sauce)
2 tsp. olive oil
1 small carrot (peeled and grated fine)
1 small piece of fresh ginger (peeled and grated or chopped)

Place olive oil and tofu in a non-stick skillet and cook on
medium until lightly browned. On a large plate place the brown
rice in the center and spread out evenly, then cover with tofu,
peas, and Bragg Liquid Aminos. Top lightly with the finely
grated carrot, fresh ginger and enjoy! This is true palate pleaser
for your carb-loading meals.

"By exercising today, I burned sixty calories. That
should take care of a peanut I had in 1962."
—*Rita Rudner*

Tuna, Rice and Spice (serves 1-2)

Protein: 58g
Fat: 19g
Carbohydrate: 116g
Calories: 873

Ingredients:
2 cups Bountiful Brown Rice (see recipe in this Chapter)
1 can water packed tuna (drained and chopped)
1/8 tsp. cinnamon
1/8 tsp. curry powder
1 small piece of fresh ginger (peeled and grated)
1 tsp. no salt mustard
1 cup green peas (steamed until tender)
1/4 small white onion (chopped)
1 tbs. flax seed oil

Place all ingredients in a mixing bowl and gently stir together
until lightly mixed. This is a spicy dish that can add some zip to
your metabolism. A fresh green salad is a great addition to this
tasty meal.

"Never go to a doctor whose office plants have died."
—Erma Bombeck

Burger and Super Spud

Protein: 45g
Fat: 22g
Carbohydrate: 41g
Calories: 532

Ingredients:
4 oz. 7% lean ground sirloin
1 oz. grated low fat cheese
1/4 small white onion (chopped)
1 green onion (washed and chopped)
1 Big-Bad-Butter Baked Potato (see recipe this chapter)
2 tbs. Mock Sour Cream (see recipe in Chapter 12)
1 tbs. fresh cilantro leaves (washed and stems removed)
1 slice of tomato

Mix the ground sirloin and the onion in a bowl, form into a patty and broil, grill or cook in a pan until browned on both sides. Cut the baked potato in half (lengthwise) and fill with grated cheese, green onion, Mock Sour Cream and top with cilantro leaves. Serve the potato and burger side by side on a plate, and top the burger with the tomato slice. This is an awesome meal that is fast, easy to make, and delicious!

Rosemary's High-Carb Stuffed Peppers (serves 2)

Per serving:
Protein: 36g
Fat: 18g
Carbohydrate: 63g
Calories: 531

Ingredients:
6 oz. 7% lean ground sirloin
1 stalk celery (washed and chopped)
1 tsp. olive oil
1 small white onion (chopped)
2 large green bell peppers (cut in half, seeds removed and steamed until tender)
1 oz. low fat cheese (grated)
1 tbs. low fat sour cream
1 tbs. dried basil
1 tbs. parsley
1 tsp. dried Rosemary
1 clove fresh garlic
2 cups "Bountiful Brown Rice" (see recipe at the beginning of this chapter)

Place onions, meat, celery, Rosemary, basil, olive oil and parsley in a non-stick skillet and cook on medium-high until the meat is lightly browned then remove from heat, mix in the Bountiful Rice and set aside. Place the steamed pepper halves in a non-stick baking pan and fill each (evenly divided) with the cooked meat and rice mixture, top with the grated cheese and bake at 325 degrees for 12-15 minutes until warm and the cheese melts. Remove from oven, and top with a dollop of low fat sour cream on each.

*"My doctor gave me six months to
live, but when I couldn't pay the bill,
he gave me six more months.*
        —*Walter Matthau*

Killer Chicken Tacos

Protein: 35g
Fat: 23g
Carbohydrate: 53g
Calories: 544

Ingredients:
1 chicken breast (prepared according to recipe in this chapter
and cut into slices)
4 corn tortillas
1/2 cup cilantro leaves
1/2 small onion (chopped)
1/2 ripe Haas avocado (peeled, pitted and cubed)
4 tbs. Salsa Fresca (see recipe in Chapter 12)

One-at-a-time place each tortilla in a skillet heated to medium-
high and cook until very warm. Fill the warm tortilla with
chicken, onion, cilantro and avocado. Do the same with each
tortilla. This is an easy meal that truly satisfies!

"I have flabby thighs, but fortunately my
stomach covers them."
—*Joan Rivers*

Mashed Potatoes and Salmon (serves 3)

Per serving:
Protein: 46g
Fat: 9g
Carbohydrate: 34g
Calories: 429

Ingredients:
3 medium Russet potatoes (washed and cut into 1 inch cubes)
1 tbs. real butter
1/4 cup nonfat plain yogurt (use water if you are dairy sensitive)
1/2 tsp. potassium based salt substitute
10 oz. fresh salmon fillets (bones removed)
4 leaves of fresh basil (chopped)
6 raw baby carrots (peeled and washed)

Mashed Potatoes
Place the potatoes in a 2-quart pan, add water until barely
covered and bring to a boil using high heat. Reduce the heat to
medium-low and cook for 10-12 minutes until the potatoes are
soft. Drain the potatoes and leave approximately 1/4 cup of the
water in the pan, add the yogurt, butter and whip the potatoes
with an electric mixer until creamy smooth adding yogurt or
water as needed for desired consistency.

Salmon
Grill the salmon fillets on an indoor or outdoor grill until flaky
and tender. Serve on a plate with the mashed potatoes, raw
baby carrots and lightly sprinkle with the chopped basil leaves.

CHAPTER 8

It's Snack Time!

Low-Carb Snacks

Low-carb snacks can be simple to fix and delicious to eat. Some basic snack options are: a chicken breast, a beef patty, a few stalks of celery, a piece of string cheese, a few slices of turkey, or a piece of chicken. Below are some other options to offer variety to the simple foods listed above.

Hoop Cheese and Celery

Protein: 22g
Fat: 0g
Carbohydrate: 5g
Calories: 108

Ingredients:
3 sticks of celery (washed)
3 oz. Hoop Cheese (from health food store)

Place the celery on a plate, scoop out the Hoop Cheese and fill each celery stick with this soft white cheese. Enjoy!

NOTE: Hoop Cheese is unique because it is the only non-fat, no-salt cheese that I am aware of. Hoop Cheese is not usually found in regular grocery stores but is sold at most health food stores. At first Hoop Cheese may taste bland to you because it is high in protein, non-fat and void of added salt.

*"Success is the result of doing what you
love to do every day of your life."*

The "Perfect" Hard Boiled Egg

Protein: 6g
Fat: 5g
Carbohydrate: 0g
Calories: 78

Ingredients:
1 cage-free, free-range, natural fed chicken egg

Pierce one end of the egg with the tip of a push-pin. Place the egg in a pan of water, so that the water is just covering the egg and heat the water to a rapid boil, then turn off the heat, cover the pan and let stand for exactly 15 minutes. Then pour off the hot water and rinse in cool water, letting the egg sit for about 5 minutes before cracking a peeling. This cooking technique will produce a beautiful hard boiled egg (or eggs) every time. I find it best to cook 6 or more eggs at a time for future meals and snacks.

*"Make every day a holiday
and every meal a banquet."*

Holiday Yogurt

Protein: 32g
Fat: 17g
Carbohydrate: 26g
Calories: 378

Ingredients:
1 cup nonfat plain yogurt
1 tbs. whey protein (vanilla)
10 drops liquid stevia
1/4 tsp. cinnamon powder
1/8 tsp. nutmeg
8 raw almonds (chopped fine in a blender)

In a bowl mix all ingredients except the chopped almonds. Top
the mixture with the chopped raw almonds and enjoy a quick,
healthy and tasty snack.
NOTE: Due to the carbohydrate content of yogurt, this recipe
is at the high end of low-carb eating and could also be listed in
the high-carb section. For a higher protein treat, use 3 tablespoons of whey protein.

*"The first telephone conversation was
between two people who were only
eighteen feet apart. It was a close call."*

Almond Butter and Celery

Protein: 5g
Fat: 19g
Carbohydrate: 10g
Calories: 215

Ingredients:
3 sticks of celery (washed)
2 tbs. no-salt, raw almond butter (from health food store)

Place the celery on a plate and fill each celery stick with the almond butter. Enjoy!

NOTE: You may also use low-fat sour cream, peanut butter, cashew butter, or any other unsalted nut butters available. One of my favorites is to lay a piece of string cheese in each stalk of celery and top it with almond butter.

*"A few months ago I was working out at a
very plush fitness club in Beverly Hills.
They had a spiral StairMaster."*

Turkey Roll-Ups

Protein: 32g
Fat: 12g
Carbohydrate: 2g
Calories: 251

Ingredients:
2 thin slices of low-salt, cooked turkey breast
2 pieces of string cheese
2 tsp. no salt mustard

Lay the turkey slices flat on a plate and cover with mustard.
Then place the string cheese at one end of the turkey slices and
roll them up so the string cheese is inside. These are fast and
easy to make and are easy to eat, even at a busy desk or when
you are on the run.

Yogurt Power

Protein: 28g
Fat: 14g
Carbohydrate: 21g
Calories: 314

Ingredients:
1 cup nonfat plain yogurt
2 tbs. protein powder (source and flavor of choice)
1 tsp. flax seed oil (optional)
6 pecans (chopped fine in a blender)

In a bowl, mix the yogurt, the protein and the flax seed oil. Top with the chopped pecans and dig in. This is a high protein taste delight!

Yogurt Power Plus

Protein: 29g
Fat: 15g
Carbohydrate: 23g
Calories: 341

Ingredients:
1 cup nonfat plain yogurt
2 tbs. protein powder (source and flavor of choice)
3 tbs. low fat sour cream
6 pecans (chopped fine in a blender)

In a bowl, mix the yogurt, the protein and sour cream. Top with the chopped pecans and dig in. With the addition of the sour cream, this is a high protein taste delight that is like a creamy dessert similar to a cheesecake!

*"Anyone who says he can see through
a woman is missing alot."*
—*Groucho Marx*

Power Cottage Cheese

Protein: 42g
Fat: 8g
Carbohydrate: 9g
Calories: 287

Ingredients:
1 cup low fat cottage cheese
2 tbs. protein powder (source and flavor of choice)
2 tbs. low fat sour cream

In a bowl, mix the cottage cheese, sour cream, and the protein powder. Stir until very well mixed. This is a high protein taste treat that is simple to make yet packs a powerful punch to the palate! For variety, try topping this dish with 2 ripe strawberries (sliced), 1/4 of an apple (peeled and cut into small pieces) or a tablespoon of fresh blueberries.

High-Carb Snacks

Banana To-Go

Protein: 1g
Fat: 1g
Carbohydrate: 27g
Calories: 104

Ingredients:
One ripe banana

Place the banana in your right hand, stem up. Grab the top of the stem with your left hand and peel it downward until half the banana is exposed. Now take a bite and enjoy!

Wanna Date?

Protein: 1g
Fat: 0g
Carbohydrate: 36g
Calories: 137

Ingredients:
6 large Medjool dates (remove pits)

Place one date at a time in your mouth start to chew slowly. You are now in heaven! Enjoy!

Dates and Almonds

Protein: 4g
Fat: 8g
Carbohydrate: 39g
Calories: 220

Ingredients:
6 large Medjool dates (pitted and cut in half)
12 raw almonds (soaked in 1 cup water for 24 hours)

Place the date halves on a plate and fill each with one almond. This unique combination of foods is very alkaline and soothing to your body because of the calcium rich almonds and potassium laced dates. The next time you want a treat on a carb-loading day, try this natural sweet snack instead of chocolate or candy. You will love it and it's guilt-free!

Chips and Salsa

Protein: 11g
Fat: 5g
Carbohydrate: 88g
Calories: 441

Ingredients:
2 cups baked corn tortilla chips
Salsa (see recipe in Chapter 12)

Place the chips on a baking sheet and warm in the oven for a few minutes on 350 degrees. Now, simply dip the chips in the salsa and enjoy. On carb-loading days, I personally love a good "chip-a-thon", especially when I am with friends and family.

Chips and Guacamole

Protein: 14g
Fat: 15g
Carbohydrate: 94g
Calories: 567

Ingredients:
2 cups baked corn tortilla chips
Guacamole (see recipe in Chapter 12)

Warm the chips in the oven, then dip the chips in the guacamole and enjoy!

Palate-Pleasing Popcorn

Protein: 2g
Fat: 1g
Carbohydrate: 13g
Calories: 61

Ingredients:
2 cups air-popped popcorn
1 tsp. Bragg's Liquid Aminos (soy sauce alternative)

Pop the corn then mist the popcorn lightly with the Bragg's Liquid Aminos, which comes in a pump spray bottle or you can buy a large bottle and put it in your own sprayer.

*"Money can't buy you happiness but it will
give you a better quality of memories."*
—Ronald Reagan

Almond Butter Power Toast

Protein: 21g
Fat: 21g
Carbohydrate: 34g
Calories: 392

Ingredients:
2 slices 100% flourless, sprouted, no salt whole grain bread
2 tbs. raw or roasted almond butter
2 tsp. Whey Protein (vanilla flavor)

Toast the bread lightly, then coat each slice (while warm) with 1 tbs. of the almond butter and sprinkle the top with whey protein.

Last week I asked my son to spell Mississippi,
and he said, "The state or the river?"

Yam-n-Avo

Protein: 3g
Fat: 6g
Carbohydrate: 40g
Calories: 217

Ingredients:
1 baked yam
1/4 large Haas avocado (peeled and cubed)

Place the baked yam on a plate and cut the yam down the
middle and fill with the cubed avocado.

CHAPTER 9

Palate Pleasing Protein Drinks

Protein drinks are a tasty, fast, easy and important means of meeting your daily protein needs. With the proper ingredients placed in a blender you can have a quick and highly nutritious meal in a matter of minutes.

Selecting a Protein Powder

There are a wide-variety of protein powders on the market, unfortunately many of them are made with low-grade proteins, sugar, sweeteners, artificial colors, artificial flavors, fructose, sucralose, aspartame, acesulfame-K, and other undesirable ingredients. When buying a high-quality protein powder, carefully read the label to insure that none of the above ingredients are in the product.

Which Protein is Best...Whey, Egg, or Soy?

In reality, of the three main proteins listed above, none of them are 100% better than the other....each is just different in its own way. Currently, whey protein is the best selling protein in America because it tastes the best of all the proteins, is easy-to-assimilate and can deliver (in high quality powders) 24 to 27 grams of solid protein per one ounce serving. The down-side to whey protein is for people who may be allergic to dairy products, including whey. Should this be the case, the next best choice in my opinion is egg white protein...

Egg White Protein...

Is also a very high quality protein powder choice and can deliver up to 24 grams of complete protein per one ounce serving. While it can be a little more difficult to blend and flavor, a high-quality egg white protein can be quite tasty and easy-to-mix when the proper ingredients are used. Should you happen to be allergic to both milk and eggs, then your next logical choice might be soy...

Soy Protein...

Derived from a unique processing of soy beans, soy protein powders have become very popular due to their estrogen supporting properties, low-cost, and better processing techniques which now yield a very high quality protein that can deliver up to 24 grams of complete protein per one ounce serving. In my opinion, of the top three proteins, soy is by far the most difficult to digest, is the hardest to flavor, is the most difficult to blend, but is lower in price, offers an alternative to milk and eggs and supports hormonal balance in women.

The Rule-of-Thumb for Selecting a Protein Powder...

A simple technique for selecting only high quality protein powders is to first make sure they don't contain any of the earlier listed "no-no" ingredients. Second, check to see that the protein content of the powder is around 24 grams of protein per ounce (not per serving). Many powders contain only 16 to 20 grams of protein per ounce meaning they are "cut" with something so you are not getting all the protein you should be in that product. Read the labels carefully and you will quickly find the best products on the market. And the final deciding factor is taste. Use the product and if it also tastes great when mixed alone in water, you have a winner!

*"The truth does not cease to exist
because it is ignored."*
—*unknown*

Low-Carb Protein Drinks

Note: All ingredients are mixed in a blender and it is usually best to add the protein powder last, after the drink is almost completely mixed. This keeps the drink from becoming too foamy because the protein can really "fluff" up the drink if added too soon. You may also increase the protein content in any of these drinks by simply adding 1 or 2 extra tablespoons of protein.

Strawberry Alarm Clock
(no this is not made with "incense and peppermint")

Protein: 25g
Fat: 8g
Carbohydrate: 15g
Calories: 221

Ingredients:
10 oz. pure water
2 tbs. vanilla protein powder
5 fresh or frozen strawberries
1 tsp. flax seed oil
12 drops liquid Stevia

Banana Hint

Protein: 25g
Fat: 15g
Carbohydrate: 10g
Calories: 196

Ingredients:
8 oz. pure water
1 oz. vanilla protein powder
1/3 ripe banana (frozen OK)
1 tsp. flax seed oil

Chocolate Lovers

Protein: 50g
Fat: 13g
Carbohydrate: 12g
Calories: 364

Ingredients:
12 oz. pure water
2 oz. chocolate whey protein
1 tsp. pure cocoa powder
1/3 frozen banana
2 tsp. flax seed oil
10 drops liquid Stevia

Tropical Treat

Protein: 25g
Fat: 8g
Carbohydrate: 10g
Calories: 196

Ingredients:
8 oz. pure water
1 oz. vanilla protein powder
1 tsp. flax seed oil
1/3 frozen banana
1 tsp. coconut extract

Just Whey

Protein:	(S) 24g	(L) 48g
Fat:	(S) 0g	(L) 0g
Carbohydrate:	(S) 3.5g	(L) 7g
Calories:	(S) 113	(L) 226

Ingredients:
small (S)...
6 oz. pure water
1 oz. whey protein (flavor of choice)

large (L)...
12 oz. pure water
2 oz. whey protein (flavor of choice)

Nutty Chocolate

Protein: 40g
Fat: 21g
Carbohydrate: 10g
Calories: 383

Ingredients:
10 oz. pure water
15 filberts
3 ice cubes (optional)
3 tbs. chocolate whey protein

Blend the filberts first until chopped fine, then add the water
(and ice if used) and then add the protein in the last 10 seconds
of blending.

Almond Dream

Protein:40 g
Fat: 9g
Carbohydrate: 9g
Calories: 274

Ingredients:
10 oz. pure water
15 raw almonds
3 ice cubes
3 tbs. vanilla protein of choice

Blend the almonds first until chopped fine, then add the water
(and ice if used) and then add the protein in the last 10 seconds
of blending.

Strawberry Cheesecake

Protein: 39g
Fat: 8g
Carbohydrate: 18g
Calories: 300

Ingredients:
10 oz. pure water
8 frozen strawberries
4 tbs. low fat sour cream
15 drops liquid stevia
3 tbs. vanilla protein powder (whey tastes the best in this drink)

Colon Power
(don't use if you are lactose intolerant)

Protein: 24g
Fat: 0g
Carbohydrate: 19g
Calories: 113

Ingredients:
8 oz. pure water
1 tbs. pure dairy whey
1 tsp. flax seed powder (or finely ground flax seeds)
2 tbs. whey protein (vanilla, chocolate or strawberry)

This is a lactose and fiber rich drink. The lactose feeds lactobacteria in your colon (the friendly bacteria) and the flax fiber sweeps the colon and stimulates lactobacteria growth and proliferation, thus helping to keep your colon balanced and in good health.

Blueberry Dream

Protein: 37g
Fat: 14g
Carbohydrate: 15g
Calories: 330

Ingredients:
10 oz. pure water
1/2 cup fresh or frozen blueberries
3 tbs. vanilla protein of choice
2 tsp. flax seed oil
15 drops liquid stevia

Macadamia Milk Shake

Protein: 40g
Fat: 22g
Carbohydrate: 13g
Calories: 410

Ingredients:
10 oz. pure water
10 raw macadamia nuts
3 tbs. protein powder of choice (whey tastes the best in this drink)

Place the macadamia nuts in the blender first and chop them fine, then add the water, then the protein last.

High-Carb Protein Drinks

The Big Banana

Protein: 49g
Fat: 7g
Carbohydrate: 34g
Calories: 390

Ingredients:
12 oz. pure water or non-fat milk
1 large ripe banana (frozen)
2 oz. whey protein (vanilla)
1 tsp. flax seed oil

Cool Carrot Power

Protein: 27g
Fat: 1g
Carbohydrate: 54g
Calories: 322

Ingredients:
12 oz. fresh carrot juice
1 apple (peeled, cored and cut into 2 inch pieces)
2 tbs. whey protein (vanilla)

Tropical Treasure

Protein: 37g
Fat: 8g
Carbohydrate: 50g
Calories: 402

Ingredients:
8 oz. pure water
1/2 cup fresh pineapple chunks (frozen OK)
1 mango (peeled, pitted and cut into slices)
3 tbs. whey protein (vanilla)
1 tsp. flax seed oil
1/2 tsp. coconut extract
8 drops liquid stevia

Chocolate Milk Shake

Protein: 36g
Fat: 6g
Carbohydrate: 39g
Calories: 311

Ingredients:
8 oz. nonfat milk
1 ripe banana (frozen)
1 tsp. pure cocoa powder
3 tbs. whey protein (chocolate)
1 tsp. flax seed oil
8 drops liquid stevia
2 ice cubes

Almond Agave Delight

Protein: 36g
Fat: 19g
Carbohydrate: 62g
Calories: 538

Ingredients:
12 oz. pure water or nonfat milk
1/4 cup raw almonds
1 ripe banana (frozen OK)
3 tbs. whey protein (vanilla or chocolate)
1 tbs. agave

Place almonds in the blender first and chop fine, then add the rest of the ingredients and blend until creamy smooth.

Strawberries and Cream

Protein: 30g
Fat: 3g
Carbohydrate: 61g
Calories: 385

Ingredients:
4 oz. pure water or nonfat milk
1 cup nonfat plain yogurt
6 ripe strawberries (frozen OK)
2 tbs. low fat sour cream
1 tbs. agave (optional)
6-10 drops liquid stevia
2 tbs. whey protein (vanilla)

*"I hate housework! You make the beds, you
do the dishes—and six months later you
have to start all over again."*
—Joan Rivers

Chapter 10

What's For Dessert?

Low-Carb Treats and Desserts

Real Whipped Cream (8 servings)

Per Serving:
Protein: 1g
Fat: 11g
Carbohydrate: 1g
Calories: 106

Ingredients:
1 cup heavy cream
2 tsp. whey protein (vanilla)
8 drops liquid stevia

Place the cream in the freezer for 15 minutes prior to whipping, then pour into a mixing bowl, add the whey and stevia and mix with electric beaters until the cream is stiff and peaks as you remove the beaters from the mix. This is a delicious low-carb delight that will add a special touch to any low-carb dessert.

*Last week I asked my son, "Where is
your homework?" He quickly replied,
"I made a paper airplane out of it,
and someone hijacked it."*

Low-Calorie Whipped Cream

Protein: 24g
Fat: 15g
Carbohydrate: 15g
Calories: 284

Ingredients:
1/2 cup nonfat plain yogurt
1/2 cup low fat sour cream
2 tbs. whey protein (vanilla)
8 drops liquid stevia

Place the yogurt and sour cream into a mixing bowl, add the
whey and stevia and mix with electric beaters until the cream is
stiff and peaks as you remove the beaters from the mix. This is a
delicious low-calorie delight that will add a special touch to any
of your favorite desserts.

*A few days ago I asked my least successful
salesperson if he had landed any new accounts.
He said, "I called on one store today and got
TWO orders...'Get out and stay out'!"*

Luscious Lemon Gelatin

Protein: 24g
Fat: 0g
Carbohydrate: 5g
Calories: 109

Ingredients:
1 cup pure water
3 cups pure water (heated to boiling)
4 envelopes unflavored gelatin
1 lemon (juiced)
25 drops liquid stevia

Sprinkle gelatin over cold water in a large bowl; let stand one
minute. Add hot water and stir until gelatin completely dis-
solves, about 5 minutes. Add the lemon juice and stevia and stir
until mixed then pour into 13 x 9 x 2-inch pan. Cover with clear
plastic wrap and refrigerate until firm, about 3 hours. To serve
cut into 3-inch squares. For a special treat, top with "Real
Whipped Cream" or "Low Calorie Whipped Cream".

*"It takes about five years for a walnut tree to
produce nuts, but this is not true of a family tree."*

Low-Carb Lemon Cheesecake (serves 6)

Protein: 10g
Fat: 13g
Carbohydrate: 8g
Calories: 181

Ingredients:
2 packets unflavored gelatin
2 cups boiling water
12 oz. low-fat sour cream
30 drops liquid stevia
1 lemon (juiced)
4 tbs. whey protein (vanilla)
1/2 cup raw almonds

In a bowl, add the boiling water and sprinkle with the gelatin,
then stir until dissolved, about 5 minutes. Add the stevia, low-
fat sour cream, lemon juice, and whey and stir with a fork until
well mixed. Pour into a 13 x 9 x 4-inch pan and refrigerate for 3
to 4 hours. To make the top crust, place the almonds in a
blender and blend until very well chopped. Once the cheesecake
has set-up, remove it from the refrigerator and cover evenly
with the chopped almonds. Cut into 3 inch squares and top each
square with 2 tsp. of "Real Whipped Cream" (see recipe at the
beginning of this chapter). This is a creamy, low-carb delight the
entire family will love.

*"Have you ever noticed the large gap
between advice and help."*

Blueberry Cottage Cheesecake

Protein: 53g
Fat: 21g
Carbohydrate: 17g
Calories: 467

Ingredients:
1 cup low fat cottage cheese
2 tbs. low fat sour cream
2 tbs. whey protein (vanilla)
5 drops liquid stevia
8 almonds (chopped fine in a blender)
2 tbs. blueberries (fresh or frozen)

In a bowl mix the cottage cheese, sour cream, stevia and protein powder until well mixed. Place this mixture into a wide
mouth wine glass or decorative bowl, sprinkle with the chopped
almonds and top with the blueberries. This is a great-tasting,
low-carb dessert that could actually be classed as a meal.

High-Carb Treats and Desserts

Cupid's Low-Calorie Pudding (serves 2)

Per Serving:
Protein: 28 grams
Fat: 1 gram
Carbohydrate: 26 grams
Calories: 220

Ingredients:
For the Pudding...
2 cups nonfat plain yogurt
1 tbs. whey protein (vanilla)
1 tbs. whey protein (strawberry)
2 ripe strawberries (washed and chopped fine)
2 ripe strawberries (washed, stems removed)
1 tsp. Agave
8 drops liquid stevia
2 wine glasses, or similar long stem glasses

In one bowl mix 1 cup of yogurt with 1 tbs. whey protein
(vanilla), and 4 drops of liquid stevia. Mix until creamy smooth
and then set aside. In another bowl, mix 1 cup of yogurt with 1
tbs. whey protein (strawberry), 2 chopped strawberries, and 4
drops liquid stevia. Mix until creamy smooth and the yogurt
turns pink with red speckles from the strawberry pieces. In a
wine glass carefully spoon in 1/2 inch of the vanilla pudding,
then a 1/2 inch of strawberry, then 1/2 inch of vanilla, then 1/2
inch of strawberry. Top one strawberry dribbled with Agave.
Repeat for the other glass. By layering the two flavors of yogurt
you produce a pink and white effect inside the glass, accented
with the ripe red strawberry on top coated with Agave.

*"I have never seen any traffic
jams on the extra mile."*

Rice Power Pudding

Protein: 27g
Fat: 6g
Carbohydrate: 77g
Calories: 463

Ingredients:
1 cup Bountiful Brown Rice (see recipe in Chapter 7)
1 cup nonfat plain yogurt
2 tbs. low fat sour cream
1 tbs. whey protein (vanilla)
6 drops liquid stevia
2 tsp. Agave

In a bowl, mix the yogurt, sour cream, stevia, whey protein and
Agave. Add the rice and stir lightly until well blended. Enjoy!

"I used to be Snow White,
but I drifted."
—*Mae West*

Almond Apple Crisp
Serves 6

Per Serving:
Protein: 5g
Fat: 13g
Carbohydrate: 32g
Calories: 184

Ingredients:
4 large red delicious apples (peeled, cored and cut into small slices)
2 tbs. Agave
1 tsp. ground cinnamon
1/2 tsp. ground nutmeg
1/2 cup raw almonds (chopped fine in a blender)
1 cup puffed rice cereal (plain puffed rice)

In a bowl mix the apples, 1 tbs. agave, cinnamon, and nutmeg. Pour the mixture into a 9 inch oiled pie pan and bake in a 350 degree preheated oven for 30-40 minutes until the apples are soft. Remove from oven and let cool for 10 minutes. Once cooled slightly, sprinkle with the almonds and top with the puffed rice and finally dribble the rice with Agave. Pop it all back in the oven and warm for about 5 minutes then serve.

"They say hot dogs can kill you.
How do you know it's not the bun?"
—Jay Leno

Big Banana Split

Protein: 9g
Fat: 12g
Carbohydrate: 62g
Calories: 365

Ingredients:
2 scoops of nonfat ice cream (Purchase at health food store)
1 large ripe banana (peeled and sliced in half lengthwise)
4 pecans (chopped)
4 almonds (chopped)

Place the banana in a bowl and part the halves, flat side facing up.
Top with side-by-side scoops of ice cream and sprinkle with the
chopped nuts). For an extra treat, top with one tablespoon of low
calorie whipped cream (see recipe earlier in this Chapter).

"If I am ever stuck on a respirator or a life support system, I definitely want to be unplugged—but not until I get down to a size eight."
—Henriette Montel

Fat Burning Chocolate Ice Cream

Protein: 49g
Fat: 1g
Carbohydrate: 9g
Calories: 237

Ingredients:
1 cup pure water
2 oz. chocolate whey protein (low carbohydrate only)
2 tsp. pure cocoa powder (unsweetened)
12 drops liquid stevia (an herb that tastes sweet)
2 cups ice cubes

Blend 45 seconds on medium high until creamy smooth and serve immediately.

Chapter 11

Fat Burning Beverages

Low-Carb Beverages

Jay's Famous Limeade

Protein: 0g
Fat: 0g
Carbohydrate: 6g
Calories: 17

Ingredients:
1 quart pure water
1 lime (juiced)
30 drops liquid Stevia
2 cups ice

Combine all ingredients in a 2 quart pitcher, stir until mixed then add ice until the pitcher is full.

*When I was a young boy my mother would ask me,
"Were you a good boy in school today?" And to this I
would reply, "Gee Mom, how much trouble can you
get into standing in a corner all day?"*

Jay's Famous Hot Chocolate

Protein: 20g
Fat: 1g
Carbohydrate: 11g
Calories: 142

Ingredients:
8 oz. pure water
1 1/4 oz. chocolate flavored whey protein
1 tsp. pure cocoa powder
12 drops liquid Stevia

Place all ingredients in a blender and lightly mix until smooth.
Pour the contents of the blender into a small sauce pan and heat
on low until "very warm" (DO NOT overheat or boil the
mixture!). Pour the hot chocolate into your favorite mug and
enjoy a high protein beverage that can help take the chill off any
winter morning.

*"I once met a weight-watcher dropout
who admitted she hadn't watched her
diet in a month of sundaes."*

Peppermint Twist Tea

Protein: 0g
Fat: 0g
Carbohydrate: 1g
Calories: 5

Ingredients:
1 peppermint tea bag
16 oz. pure water
1 lemon wedge
15 drops liquid Stevia

Place water in a saucepan and heat to boiling, then add tea bag
and let steep for five minutes. Next, squeeze the juice of the
lemon wedge into the tea and add the Stevia. Serve in your
favorite mug and enjoy a very soothing and refreshing, caffeine-
free tea, that is rich in vitamin C.

"My formula for success?
Rise early, work late, strike oil."
—J. Paul Getty

"My formula for success?
Rise early, love your work, burn fat."
—Jay Robb

Low-Carb Lemonade

Protein: 0g
Fat: 0g
Carbohydrate: 8g
Calories: 22

Ingredients:
1 quart pure water
1 medium Meyer lemon
30 drops liquid Stevia
2 cups ice

Combine all ingredients in a 2 quart pitcher, stir until mixed then add ice until the pitcher is full.

"If it weren't for the last minute,
nothing would get done."

Almond Milk

Protein: 10g
Fat: 25g
Carbohydrate: 9g
Calories: 283

Ingredients:
1/3 cup raw almonds
1 cup pure water

Place the raw almonds in a blender and pour in just enough water to cover the almonds. Blend until the almonds become creamy smooth, almost like a thin paste (this may require 1-2 minutes of blending but is very important. Turn off the blender and add the remainder of the water, then lightly buzz until blended but not foamy. Pour into your favorite glass and enjoy! This is a great calcium-rich beverage that is an alternative to cow's milk.

*"Only astronauts are happy to
be down and out."*

Jay's Famous 11-Up

Protein: 0g
Fat: 0g
Carbohydrate: 5g
Calories: 16

Ingredients:
12 oz. plain sparkling water
1/4 fresh lime
1/4 fresh lemon
15 drops liquid Stevia
4 cubes ice

Squeeze the juice of the lime and lemon into a large glass, then add the Stevia and stir until mixed. Gently pour the sparkling water into the glass to save the effervescence, then fill the glass with ice and enjoy the perfect alternative to one of America's favorite sugar-laced soft drinks.

"Sex appeal is 50% what you've got and
50% what people think you've got."
—Sophia Loren

Sparkling Zinger-Stinger

Protein: 0
Fat: 0
Carbohydrate: 0
Calories: 0

Ingredients:
1/2 cup Celestial Seasonings Red Zinger tea (brewed as directed on box)
1 cup plain sparkling water
8 drops liquid stevia

Place all ingredients in a 16 oz. glass and stir gently. May be served with ice for a very cold drink.

"The secret to longevity is to keep breathing."
—*Sophie Tucker*

High-Carb Beverages

Papaya Sunrise

Protein: 4g
Fat: 0g
Carbohydrate: 56g
Calories: 229

Ingredients:
4 oranges (juiced)
1 small Hawaiian papaya or 1/2 large Mexican papaya
12 drops liquid Stevia (optional but really makes the OJ sweet!)

Cut the papaya and remove the seeds with a spoon, then carefully slice away the outer skin. Place the orange juice, Stevia and papaya in a blender and buzz for about 30 seconds until creamy smooth. This is an island delight I discovered on the North Shore of Oahu in 1985. My wife, Rosemary, and I were married at Waimea Falls (on the North Shore) in 1988 and celebrated with a Papaya Sunrise before flying to Maui for our honeymoon. This is a great body-cleanser and carb-loading breakfast!

*"You know it's going to be a rough day
when you see the '60 Minutes' camera
crew setting up outside your office."*
—Unknown

Here Comes the Sun
(Very Sweet, Sugar-Free OJ)

Protein: 0g
Fat: 0g
Carbohydrate: 13g
Calories: 56

Ingredients:
3 ripe oranges
10 drops liquid Stevia

Juice the oranges then place the juice and Stevia in a blender
and buzz for 5 seconds to mix the juice and Stevia. You won't
believe how sweet the Stevia makes the juice no matter how
tart the juice was to begin with!

*"My first sign of maturity was
when I discovered the volume
knob also turns to the left."*

Orange-Grapefruit Delight

Protein: 3g
Fat: 0g
Carbohydrate: 58g
Calories: 250

Ingredients:
2 oranges
2 grapefruits
8 drops liquid Stevia
2 tsp. Agave (warmed slightly)

Juice the oranges and grapefruit and place in a blender with
Stevia and Agave, then blend for a few seconds until well
mixed. Mmmm Good!

*"Living your dream is a lot more fun
than just having a dream."*

Hi-Carb Hot Chocolate

Protein: 22g
Fat: 1g
Carbohydrate: 35g
Calories: 238

Ingredients:
6 oz. pure water or skim milk
1 oz. chocolate whey protein
1 tsp. pure cocoa powder
1 tbs. Agave
6 drops liquid Stevia

Place all ingredients in a blender and buzz a few moments until well blended. Pour into a saucepan and warm slowly until hot but not boiling. Add the Agave and stir with a spoon until mixed, then pour into your favorite mug and enjoy!

*"To get back on your feet,
miss two car payments."*

Natural Chocolate Milk

Protein: 30g
Fat: 6g
Carbohydrate: 35g
Calories: 284

Ingredients:
6 oz. pure water or skim milk
1 oz. chocolate whey protein
1 tsp. flax oil
1 tsp. pure cocoa powder
2 tsp. Agave (warmed slightly)

Place all ingredients in a blender and buzz briefly to mix. Pour into a glass and enjoy a healthy, chocolate milk alternative.

*"Successful dieting is just
mind over platter."*

Red-Eye Shot

Protein: 1g
Fat: 0g
Carbohydrate: 17g
Calories: 71

Ingredients:
3 oranges (juiced)
6 ripe strawberries (washed, stems removed)
12 drops liquid Stevia
1 small piece of fresh ginger (peeled and grated)

Place all in a blender and buzz until blended well then pour into your favorite glass. This unique blend offers quite a "zip" due to the presence of the ginger.

When I first began dating as a young man, it wasn't long until I gained the reputation as a real "Don Yawn".

Tropical Pleasure

Protein: 4g
Fat: 1g
Carbohydrate: 77g
Calories: 303

Ingredients:
4 oranges (juiced)
1 mango (peeled, pit removed and cut into pieces)
1 small papaya (seeds and skin removed)
12 drops liquid Stevia
1 tsp. coconut extract

Place all ingredients in a blender and blend for 30 seconds or more until well mixed and smooth. This is a great tropical tasting smoothie that is all natural, very cleansing and very refreshing on a carb-loading morning.

"A crab is a fiddler on the reef."

Tangerine Dream

Protein: 3g
Fat: 8g
Carbohydrate: 21g
Calories: 152

Ingredients:
5 medium tangerines (juiced)
10 raw almonds (soaked 24 hours in water)

Place the soaked almonds in a blender and barely cover them with water, then blend until creamy smooth, added water as needed to make the mixture smooth. Next, add the tangerine juice to the blender and blend until well mixed. Pour into your favorite glass and enjoy a creamy smooth, tangerine taste delight.

*"I heard the other day that the man who
invented the electric razor had worked on
the idea since he was a little shaver."*

Almond Date Milk Shake

Protein: 4g
Fat: 8g
Carbohydrate: 33g
Calories: 197

Ingredients:
5 Medjool dates (pitted and cut in half)
10 raw almonds (soaked 18 hours in water)

Place the almonds in a blender and add water until the almonds
are just barely covered. Blend until creamy smooth. Next, add
the dates to the blender and just enough water to cover all,
blend until velvety smooth then add just enough water to make
a nice thick milk shake. Ice can also be added for a nice frozen
effect.

" A bedbug is an undercover agent."

Agave Almond Milk Shake

Protein: 7g
Fat: 18g
Carbohydrate: 16g
Calories: 243

Ingredients:
1/4 cup raw almonds
1/2 cup water
2 tsp. Agave (warmed)
1/8 tsp. pure vanilla extract

Place the almonds in a blender and grind them into a fine powder, then add just enough water to cover them and continue blending into a smooth paste. Add the remainder of the water, warm Agave, and vanilla then blend together to form a heavenly dairy-free milk shake.

*"Give a dandelion an inch, and
it takes over a yard."*

Banana Milk Shake

Protein: 10g
Fat: 6g
Carbohydrate: 56g
Calories: 297

Ingredients:
1 cup low-fat on skim milk
1 ripe frozen banana
1 tbs. Agave
1 tsp. vanilla extract
1 tsp. flax seed oil

Place all in a blender and blend until creamy smooth. If you tolerate milk and dairy products, this is a delicious alternative to the traditional ice cream based milk shakes that are helping keep the world "round".

*"Sometimes it rains cats and dogs, but it
would be worse if it hailed taxis."*

Banana Almond Milk Shake

Protein: 17g
Fat: 14g
Carbohydrate: 63g
Calories: 446

Ingredients:
1 cup pure water
1/4 cup raw almonds (soaked 18 hours in water)
1 frozen banana
1 tbs. Agave (optional)
1 tsp. vanilla

Place almonds in a blender, barely cover them with water and
blend to a creamy paste. Add the vanilla, frozen banana and
remaining water and blend until thick and rich, then pour in the
Agave and mix a few more seconds. Serve in your favorite glass
and eat with a spoon or drink like a milk shake. For a thinner
shake, add more water.

Five Fat Burning Tips

1 Stop eating <u>3 hours</u> before bedtime.

2 Drink <u>three quarts</u> or more of pure water each day.

3 Control <u>calories and carbohydrate foods</u> by following The Fat Burning Diet eating plan.

4 Abstain from food for <u>12 hours each day</u>.
This means that if your last meal the day before was eaten at 9:00 PM, your first meal or snack the next day could come no sooner than 9:00 AM.

5 <u>Take your body temperature</u> several times each day to make sure your metabolism is not <u>shut down</u>. During the day your temperature should be around 98.6 degrees Fahrenheit. If it is lower than this, <u>your metabolism may be slow</u> and your chance of burning fat is low. (See Chapter 7 in my book, The Fat Burning Diet, to see what to do if your temperature is low.)

Chapter 12

Low-Carb Super Salads

The Ginger-Binger

Protein: 5g
Fat: 16g
Carbohydrate: 16g
Calories: 206

Ingredients:
2 cups Romaine lettuce (washed and cut into salad-size pieces)
1/8 white onion (sliced very thin)
6 cherry tomatoes (washed and cut in half)
1/2 medium Haas avocado (diced)
1 small piece of fresh ginger root (peeled and finely diced)

Place the lettuce in a medium size bowl and top with onion, tomatoes, avocado and ginger, then toss lightly. No need for dressing because the fresh avocado does the trick! This is a great salad to serve with any meat or protein dish.

"I'm tellin' ya, I get no respect. When I was
in Switzerland, I got an obscene yodel."
—Rodney Dangerfield

Apple-Cilantro Supreme

Protein: 4g
Fat: 16g
Carbohydrate: 20g
Calories: 216

Ingredients:
2 cups butter leaf lettuce (washed and cut into salad-size pieces)
1/4 red bell pepper (chopped)
1/2 granny smith apple (washed, cored and diced into 1/2 inch pieces)
1/4 cup fresh cilantro leaves
1/2 medium Haas avocado (diced)
1 stalk celery (strings removed, washed and diced finely)

Place lettuce in a large bowl, then top with red peppers, celery, apple, cilantro and avocado. Toss lightly and dig in! This is a very tasty salad that goes great with any main dish.

"A diet is responsible eating for practicing girth control."

Walnutty Salad

Protein: 15g
Fat: 14g
Carbohydrate: 24g
Calories: 245

Ingredients:
2 cups red leaf lettuce (washed and cut into salad-size pieces)
1 large carrot (grated)
1/8 head of red cabbage (shredded fine)
1 green onion (chopped)
6 raw walnut halves
1 oz. grated low-fat cheese (optional)
1 small red tomato (chopped)

Place lettuce in a bowl then top in the following order: cabbage, carrots, green onion, tomato, cheese, and walnuts. Dress lightly with a few sprinkles of Balsamic vinegar and dig in! This one is a real palate pleaser!

"A friend of mine is a glassblower who does beautiful work. One day he accidentally inhaled and got a pane in the stomach."

Super Spinach Salad

Protein: 12g
Fat: 12g
Carbohydrate: 9g
Calories: 182

Ingredients:
2 cups loosely packed baby spinach leaves
3 walnut halves (chopped fine)
1/4 Haas avocado (cut into small cubes)
2 hard boiled eggs (yolk removed, and thin sliced)
1/4 lime wedge
2 mushrooms (washed and sliced)

Place spinach in a large bowl and then top in the following order: mushrooms, eggs, avocado, walnuts then dribble the juice of the lime over the top.

"One of my first jobs was in a bicycle repair shop. Within a few weeks I was known as the city's spokes-person."

Tangy Slaw Salad

Protein: 3g
Fat: 4g
Carbohydrate: 18g
Calories: 108

Ingredients:
2 cups green cabbage (very finely shredded)
1 seedless tangerine (separate into individual sections, then cut each section in half)
1 red radish (thin sliced)
1 tbs. low-salt mayonnaise
1/2 tsp. celery seed
1/4 small white onion (chopped)

Place cabbage and mayonnaise in a large bowl and mix well. Add the remaining ingredients and toss lightly, then ENJOY!

"Mickey Mouse may have
hypoglycemia because I hear he has
frequent Disney spells."

Digestive Enhancer

Protein: 3g
Fat: 5g
Carbohydrate: 7g
Calories: 75

Ingredients:
1 cup escarole or endive (washed and chopped)
1 cup Romaine lettuce (washed and cut into salad size pieces)
1/2 cup baby spinach (stems removed)
2 tsp. dulse flakes
1 small piece of fresh ginger root (peeled and grated)
2 mushrooms (washed and sliced)
2 tsp. raw apple cider vinegar
1 tsp. flax seed oil or olive oil

Place all ingredients (except oil and vinegar) in a large bowl and toss lightly. Top with oil and vinegar and you have a superb salad that will help stimulate a healthy appetite and enhance your digestion. The bitter salad greens are the secret that stimulate bile secretion and other digestive juices, plus the ginger enhances the entire digestive process and stokes the metabolism. This salad is best eating first, then begin your main course 10 minutes later.

Chapter 13

Low-Carb Salad Dressings

Oil and Balsamic Vinegar (12 servings)

Per Serving:
Protein: 0g
Fat: 9g
Carbohydrate: 0g
Calories: 80

Ingredients:
1/4 cup extra virgin olive oil
1/4 cup flax seed oil
3 tbs. Balsamic vinegar

Put oil and vinegar in a glass bottle and shake well. Use one tablespoon on your salad as a simple, fast and easy dressing.

*I visited my acupuncturist last week for a
pain in my left shoulder. After one
treatment I was 90% improved so I said,
"Thank you for a jab well done!"*

Creamy Garlic (10 servings)

Per Serving:
Protein: 6g
Fat: 3g
Carbohydrate: 9g
Calories: 84

Ingredients:
1 quart non-fat plain yogurt
12 drops liquid stevia
2 tbs. olive oil
1 small white onion (chopped)
2 cloves garlic (chopped)
1 small piece of fresh ginger (peeled and chopped fine)

Place all ingredients in a bowl and mix until very well blended.
Store in the refrigerator and use as a salad dressing as needed.
This recipe is also an excellent dip for fresh veggies.

*"Have you ever noticed that old age is
about 15 years older than you are?"*

Low-Calorie Thick Ranch Dressing (6 servings)

Per Serving
Protein: 5g
Fat: 4g
Carbohydrate: 7g
Calories: 70

Ingredients:
2 cups nonfat plain yogurt
1 tbs. flax seed oil
6 drops liquid stevia
1 tbs. dried onion
1 tbs. dried parsley
1/2 tsp. garlic powder (not garlic salt)
1/2 tsp. dried basil
1/2 tsp. dried thyme
1/4 tsp. fresh ground black pepper
1/2 tsp. potassium based salt substitute

Place all ingredients in a large bowl and mix until well blended
and creamy smooth. This is an outstanding dressing that is void
of the chemicals, sugars, and salt that a typical store-bought
ranch dressing would contain. For an extra zip, try adding one
clove of finely chopped fresh garlic.

"One day I was so busy finishing my next book that I got my word processor mixed up with my food processor. It was the first time I ever remember mincing my words."

Chapter 14

Fat Burning Sauces, Gravies and Condiments

Salsa Fresca

Protein: 6g
Fat: 2g
Carbohydrate: 35g
Calories: 149

Ingredients:
1 medium white onion (peeled and chopped)
1 green mild chili pepper (chopped)
1 small jalepeno pepper (chopped)
2 medium size ripe tomatoes (chopped)
1/2 lime (juiced)
1/2 cup fresh cilantro leaves (washed, stems removed)

In a bowl, mix the tomatoes, onions, chili pepper, cilantro and lemon juice. Add the jalepeno pepper last and only add as much as you personally like. Jalepeno peppers can make the salsa too hot, so go slow!

"In the beginner's mind there are many possibilities, but in the experts there are few."
—*Shunryu Suzuki*

*"Mealtime is that period of the day when
the kids sit down to continue eating."*

Jay's 3 Alarm Salsa

Protein: 7g
Fat: 2g
Carbohydrate: 40g
Calories: 171

Ingredients:
1 medium white onion (peeled and chopped)
1 green mild chili pepper (chopped)
2 small jalepeno peppers (chopped)
1 serrano red chili pepper (chopped)
2 medium size ripe tomatoes (chopped)
1 small piece of fresh ginger (peeled and grated)
1/2 lime (juiced)
1/2 cup fresh cilantro leaves (washed, stems removed)

In a bowl, mix the tomatoes, onions, chili pepper, cilantro and
lemon juice. Add the jalepeno and serrano peppers last and only
add as much as you personally like. Jalepeno and serrano
peppers can make the salsa too hot, so go slow!

Palate Pleasing Pesto (dairy-free, serves 4)

Per Serving
Protein: 8g
Fat: 19g
Carbohydrate: 7g
Calories: 204

Ingredients:
1 large ripe Haas avocado (peeled and pit removed)
1 cup fresh basil leaves
1 tbs. fresh lime or lemon juice
2 garlic cloves (minced)
1/3 cup raw pine nuts
1 tsp. extra virgin olive oil

Place all ingredients in a food processor and mix for a minute or two until will blended. You may need to scrape the sides of the processor and add a few drops of water to help in the blending process. (You can also make this in a blender, but you will need more water to make it blend easier, and you must scrape the sides of the blender frequently.) Use immediately and any unused pesto should be placed in an air tight container and stored in the refrigerator. To keep the unused portion from becoming discolored, place a piece of plastic wrap directly over the top the pesto, then put on the lid. The plastic wrap will keep the air from directly contacting the pesto. This pesto is delicious over wheat-free pasta made from rice or corn. Due to its high fat content, a little goes a long way, but because it is so flavorful...it really doesn't take much to satisfy your taste buds.

*"You ever wonder if illiterate people
get the full effect of alphabet soup?"*
—*John Mendoza*

Guacamole (6 servings)

Per Serving:
Protein: 2g
Fat: 10g
Carbohydrate: 8g
Calories: 119

Ingredients:
2 ripe Haas avocados (skin and pit removed)
1/2 cup fresh cilantro leaves (washed and stems removed)
1/2 fresh lime (juiced)
1 small ripe tomato (chopped)
1/2 small white onion (chopped)

In a bowl, mash the avocado with a fork until creamy smooth.
Add the tomato, lime, onion and cilantro leaves and mix until
well blended.

"Cured ham? No thanks, pal. Cured of what?
What if it has a relapse on my plate?"
—*Tommy Sledge*

Balanced Butter (20 servings)

Per Serving:
Protein: 0g
Fat: 10g
Carbohydrate: 0g
Calories: 90

Ingredients:
1 stick (1/2 cup) raw or pasteurized real butter (soft at room temperature)
1/2 cup flax seed oil

In a bowl, whip the butter and flax oil together until well mixed, then refrigerate until firm, then use like butter. Not for cooking or baking because the Omega-3 essential fatty acids in flax oil are sensitive to light and heat.

"Success in life simply means you are living your dream. And to live your dream requires that you first admit what your dream is. Once you acknowledge your dream, you can set goals and take action to make that dream come true."

No-Butter Better Butter Blend (say that fast 3 times)
(20 servings)
Per Serving:
Protein: 0g
Fat: 7g
Carbohydrate: 0g
Calories: 68

1/2 cup unrefined coconut butter (edible food grade)
1/2 cup flax seed oil

In a pan, lightly warm the coconut butter until it is a liquid, then let cool. Add the flax oil to the pan, mix and refrigerate in a glass container until hard like butter. May be used anytime butter is desired. Not for cooking or baking because the Omega-3 essential fatty acids in flax oil are sensitive to light and heat.

"I live in an area of San Diego where a lot of successful people reside. Even the kids are extremely enterprising. Just last week I saw a neighbor boy running a lemonade stand. This kid would give the first glass away for free and charge $25 for a refill...which contained the antidote."

Homemade Nutty Nut Butter Blend (12 servings)

Per Serving:
Protein: 2g
Fat: 10g
Carbohydrate: 3g
Calories: 108

Ingredients:
1/2 cup raw almonds
1/2 cup raw macadamia nuts
1/2 cup raw pecans

Run all the raw nuts through a Champion Juicer with the blank plate in place for grinding nut butters. Store the fresh made nut butters in a container in the refrigerator. Single nut butters (i.e. almond only, macadamia only) or other combinations may also be made.

Have you ever seen these places that feature fish sandwiches? I always think, "Well, that's kind of general." I wouldn't order something called a meat sandwich; at least not without a couple of follow-up questions: "Does anyone know where the meat came from? Are any of the waitresses missing?"
—*George Carlin*

Omega-3 Mayonnaise (18 servings)

Per Serving:
Protein: 0g
Fat: 10g
Carbohydrate: 0g
Calories: 91

Ingredients:
2 soft boiled eggs (cooked in boiling water for 1 minute)
2 tablespoons lemon juice
1/2 cup extra virgin olive oil
1/4 cup flax seed oil
1 tsp. mustard

Place the eggs, lemon juice, and mustard in a food processor and blend for 15 to 30 seconds until well mixed. Using the attachment that allows you to add liquids, slowly add the oils while the motor is running until the mixture thickens. This no salt, Omega-3 mayonnaise may then be stored in the refrigerator for about 7 days. Because it contains egg yolks, refrigerate the mayonnaise very quickly after preparing the recipe and keep it refrigerated.

*"Goals and dreams require a clear
and well devised set of plans. These
plans are broken into a series of
projects that, when complete, can
make any dream come true."*

Terrific Turkey or Charming Chicken Gravy

Per Serving (18 servings)
Protein: 0g
Fat: 10g
Carbohydrate: 1g
Calories: 95

Ingredients:
1 cup drippings from roasting a whole turkey or chicken, or a
turkey or chicken breast
1 1/2 tbs. brown rice flour
1/2 tsp. fresh ground black pepper
1/2 tsp. potassium based salt substitute

Mix or whisk together the drippings and flour in a small saucepan or skillet. Cook on low to medium heat until thickened,
then reduce heat and simmer on warm for 10 minutes. You may
thin the gravy by adding water if needed, or thicken it by adding
more rice flour.

*"I used to love fast food, but that stuff will kill
you. Why do you think that fast-food joints and
emergency rooms are both open 24 hours a
day? And they both have drive-throughs."*
—Joel Warshaw

Pasta Sauce
Makes 2 cups

Protein: 5g
Fat: 1g
Carbohydrate: 32g
Calories: 141

Ingredients:
3 cups fresh tomatoes (peeled and diced)
1 medium onion (finely chopped)
1 tbs. olive oil
2 tbs. Balsamic vinegar
3 garlic cloves (finely chopped)
1/2 cup basil (finely chopped)
a few shakes of fresh ground black pepper
1/2 tsp. Nu-Salt salt substitute

Saute onions in olive oil until tender and moist. Add in the
tomatoes, Balsamic vinegar, and bring to a mild boil, then
reduce the heat and cook until most of the liquid is gone. Stir in
the basil, Nu-Salt and pepper and cover unheated for about 20
minutes to let the flavors blend. This sauce is great over wheat-
free pasta, pizza or anytime you want a great-tasting pasta
sauce.

"You know you're fat when you can pinch an inch on your forehead."
—*John Mendoza*

Jay's Zippy Dip (8 servings)

Per Serving:
Protein: 7g
Fat: 2g
Carbohydrate: 11g
Calories: 59

Ingredients:
1 quart non-fat plain yogurt
1 tbs. flax seed oil
1 small white onion (chopped)
3 cloves fresh garlic (peeled and chopped)
12 drops liquid stevia (helps remove the tartness of yogurt)
1 tsp. No Salt (salt substitute)
1/4 cup fresh cilantro leaves (washed, stems removed)
small piece of fresh ginger (peeled and grated)

Place all ingredients in a bowl and mix. This is a great dip with raw veggies, rice cracker chips, baked corn chips or baked potato chips.

*"I haven't spoken to my wife in years—
I didn't want to interrupt her."*
—Rodney Dangerfield

*"You may marry the man of your dreams,
ladies, but fourteen years later you're
married to a couch that burps."*
—Roseanne

Mock Sour Cream (16 servings)

Per Serving:
Protein: 3g
Fat: 1g
Carbohydrate: 4g
Calories: 40

Ingredients:
1 quart non-fat plain yogurt
12 drops liquid stevia
1 tbs. flax seed oil
1/2 tsp. No-Salt or Nu-Salt potassium based salt substitute
(optional)

Mix all ingredients in a bowl until creamy smooth, then use just like sour cream.

"In Heaven an Angel is nobody in particular."
—George Bernard Shaw

Fat Burning Food Chart

Abbreviation Key: Amt. = Amount; Prot.= Protein; Carb.= Carbohydrate; Cal.= calories; g.= Grams; oz. = ounce; tsp.= teaspoon; tbs.= tablespoon; C = cup.

Note: All meats listed are broiled, roasted or baked, not fried. All amounts listed are approximations.

FOOD GROUP I

Protein Foods	Amt.	Cal.	Prot./g.	Carb./g.	Fat /g.
Swordfish	3.75 oz.	164	27	0	5.5
Ocean Perch	4.5 oz.	128	24	0	2
Tuna (water packed)	4 oz.	120	28	0	2
Chicken Breast	3. oz.	198	29	0	7.5
Skinless Chicken Thigh	3.5 oz.	216	27	0	11
Skinless Chicken Meat	4 oz.	215	33	0	8.5
Skinless Turkey (dark)	4 oz.	210	32	0	8
Skinless Turkey (light)	4 oz.	160	34	0	1.5
Ground Turkey Patty	2.3 oz.	194	23	0	11
Beef Round Steak	7 oz.	470	52	0	27
Beef Sirloin -choice	4 oz.	320	32	0	21
Beef-T-Bone Steak	4 oz.	322	26	0	23
Beef, Lean Ground	3 oz.	240	24	0	15
Beef, Xtr Lean Ground	3.5 oz.	265	28	0	16
Deer/Venison	4 oz.	178	34	0	4
Large Whole Egg	1 each	75	6.25	.5	5
Egg White (cooked)	1 each	16.5	3.5	.35	0
Egg Yolk (cooked)	1 each	59	2.75	.3	5

FOOD GROUP II

Vegetables	Amt.	Cal.	Prot./g.	Carb./g	Fat/g.
Asparagus Spears (raw)	6 each	20	2	4	.2
Broccoli (raw)	4 oz.	32	3.5	6	.4
Brussels Sprouts (raw)	4 oz.	49	4	10	.3
Cabbage (raw)	4 oz.	28	1.5	6	.3

Vegetables	Amt.	Cal.	Prot./g.	Carb./g	Fat/g.
Carrots (raw)	1 each	31	.75	7	.1
Cauliflower (raw)	4 oz.	28	2.25	6	.3
Celery (raw)	4 oz.	18	1	4	.2
Collards (raw)	4 oz.	35	1.75	8	.25
Corn on Cob (boiled)	1 each	71	2.5	17	.5
Cucumber Slices	1 oz.	3	.2	.5	.3
Dandelion Greens (raw)	4 oz.	51	3	10	.8
Escarole (raw)	4. oz.	19	1.5	3.75	.2
Kale (raw)	4 oz.	57	3.75	11	.8
Kohlrabi (raw)	3.5 oz.	25	1.5	6	.1
Iceberg Lettuce (raw)	1.5 oz.	5	.5	1	.75
Romaine Lettuce (raw)	1 oz.	3	.3	.5	.04
Butter Lettuce	1 each	45	3.75	8.5	.74
Mustard Greens (raw)	4 oz.	30	3	5.5	.2
Onions (raw)	4 oz.	43	1.5	10	.2
Parsley (chopped-raw)	1 tbs.	1.4	.1	.2	.03
Parsnips (raw-sliced)	1 tbs.	6.25	.1	1.5	.03
Green Peas (raw)	4 oz.	190	12	35	.5
Green Bell Peppers	1 oz.	7.75	.25	1.75	.05
Chili Peppers (hot-red)	1 oz.	11	.6	2.75	.06
Radishes (red-raw)	4 each	3	.1	.6	.1
Spinach (raw)	4 oz.	25	3.25	4	.4
Summer Squash (raw)	8 oz.	20	1	5.5	.1
Tomato (medium, raw)	1 each	26	1	5.75	.4

FOOD GROUP III

Fresh Fruit	Amt.	Cal.	Prot./g.	Carb./g.	Fat/g.
Apple (medium)	1 each	81	.275	21	.5
Applesauce (unswtnd.)	4 oz.	48	.2	13	.06
Apricots (pitted)	3 each	51	1.5	12	.4
Avocado (raw)	6 oz.	306	3.75	12	30
Banana (medium, raw)	4 oz.	104	1.2	26	.5
Blackberries (raw)	8 oz.	118	1.6	29	.9
Blueberries (raw)	8 oz.	127	1.52	32	.9
Red Raspberries (raw)	8 oz.	111	2	26	1.25
Strawberries (raw)	8 oz.	68	1.4	16	.8
Cantaloupe (raw)	12 oz.	119	3	29	1
Grapes (raw)	.5 cup	53	1	12	.75
Grapefruit (medium	.5 each	37	.75	9	.1
Peach (medium)	1 each	37	.6	10	.1

Fresh Fruit	Amt.	Cal.	Prot./g.	Carb./g.	Fat/g.
Pear (medium)	1 each	98	.7	25	.7
Pineapple (raw)	8 oz.	111	.9	28	1
Plum (medium)	1 each	36	.5	9	.4
Prunes (dried)	4. oz.	270	3	71	.6
Honeydew (raw)	12 oz.	99	1.3	26	.3
Kiwifruit (raw)	1 each	46	.75	11	.3
Mango (medium, raw)	.5 each	67	.5	18	.3
Orange (medium, raw)	1 each	62	1.25	16	.2
Watermelon (6"x 2" slc)	1 each	170	3	40	1.3

FOOD GROUP IV

Fats and Oils	Amt.	Cal.	Prot./g.	Carb./g	Fat/g.
Almonds (raw)	4 oz.	668	23	23	60
Brazil Nuts (raw)	4 oz.	744	17	14.5	76
Cashews	1 oz.	163	4.5	9	13
Coconut (dried)	4 tbs.	129	1.5	5	13
Macadamia Nuts	1 oz.	199	2.5	4	21
Mixed Nuts (roasted)	1 oz.	168	5	7	15
Peanuts (dry roasted)	4 oz.	663	27	24	56
Pecan Halves (raw)	1 oz.	189	2.2	5	19
Pine Nuts (raw)	1 oz.	146	7	4	14
Pistachio Nuts (raw).	4 oz.	655	23	28	55
Pumpkin Seeds (raw)	1 oz.	126	5	15	5
Sesame Seeds (raw)	1 oz.	162	5	7	14
Sunflower Seeds (raw)	1 oz.	161	6.5	5	14
Walnuts (English, raw)	10 each	130	3	4	12
Butter	1 tbs.	102	.1	0	11.5
Flax Seed Oil	1 tbs.	128	0	0	14
Olive Oil	1 tbs.	119	0	0	13.5
Safflower Oil	1 tbs.	120	0	0	13.5
Canola Oil	1 tbs.	120	0	0	13.5
Wheat Germ Oil	1 tbs.	120	0	0	13.5

FOOD GROUP V

Dairy Products	Amt.	Cal.	Prot./g.	Carb./g	Fat/g
Whole Milk	8 oz.	138	7.5	10.5	7.5
Half and Half Cream	1 tbs.	20	.5	.5	1.75
Whipping Cream	1 tbs.	51	.3	.5	5.5
Sour Cream	1 tbs.	31	.5	.5	3

Dairy Products	Amt.	Cal.	Prot./g.	Carb./g	Fat/g
Soy Milk (plain)	8 oz.	75	6	4	4
Yogurt (nonfat, plain)	8 oz.	126	13	17	.4
Yogurt (whole, plain)	8 oz.	139	8	11	7
Cheese (Colby)	1 oz.	111	7	.75	9
Cottage Cheese (reg.)	8 oz.	233	28	6	10
Cream Cheese	1 oz.	99	2	.75	10
Blue Cheese	1 oz.	100	6	.5	8
Cheddar Cheese	1 oz.	114	7	.35	9

The Following Foods are for "Carb-Load" and "FREE-Meal" Days

FOOD GROUP VI

Starches	Amt.	Cal.	Prot./g .	Carb./g.	Fat/g.
Brown Rice (cooked)	8 oz.	251	6	52	2
Oatmeal (plain)	8 oz.	133	5.75	23	2
Corn Tortilla	1 each	67	1.75	14	.75
Pancake (wh. wht, 5")	1 each	108	4.5	15	3.5
Bread (wh. wht, slice)	1 each	86	3.5	16	1.5
Bagel (plain)	1 each	187	7	36	1
Corn Muffin	2 oz.	173	3.5	29	5
Waffle (plain)	1 each	218	5	26	10
Popcorn (air pop, plain)	2 oz.	216	7	44	2.5
Lasagna Pasta (cooked)	4 oz.	160	5.5	32	.75
Pasta Spirals (cooked)	4 oz.	160	5.5	32	.75
Potato (baked)	7 oz.	220	5	32	.2
Squash (winter, baked)	8 oz.	88	2	20	1.5
Sweet Potato (baked)	4 oz.	60	1	14	.1

Beans	Amt.	Cal.	Prot./g.	Carb./g.	Fat/g
Navy Beans (boiled)	8 oz.	322	20	60	1.5
Black Beans (boiled)	8 oz.	299	20	54	1
Split Peas (boiled)	8 oz.	267	19	48	1
Lima Beans (boiled)	8 oz.	261	18	47	1
Kidney Beans (boiled)	8 oz.	288	20	52	1
Tofu (plain)	3.5 oz.	75	8	2	5

In Closing

A Final Word
From Jay Robb

I sincerely hope you have enjoyed my Fat Burning Diet COOK BOOK. By applying these recipes into your life you can truly change the way you look, feel and think.

Should you need any more information on burning fat, weight loss, fitness or health, please call our offices at 1-877 JAY ROBB, and we'll send you our latest catalog and information packet. If you are on the web, please visit our web site at jayrobb.com and check out everything we offer that can help you stay lean for a lifetime.

May God richly bless you on your journey...

Naturally,

Jay Robb

"There's no way that moving in with your parents
is a sign that your life is on track."
—Jerry Seinfeld

Appendixes

For Your Convenience

Approximate Metric Conversions

Abbreviations: ounce = oz.; pound = lb.; teaspoon = tsp.; tablespoon = tbs.; cup = c; quart = qt; grams = g; milliliter = ml; centimeter = cm; liter = l

WEIGHTS

US	Metric
1 oz	28 g
2 oz	57 g
3 oz	85 g
4 oz (1/4 lb)	114 g
5 oz	142 g
6 oz.	170 g
8 oz. (1/2 lb)	227 g
12 oz (3/4 lb)	340 g
14 oz	397 g
16 oz (1 lb)	454 g
32 oz (2 lb)	908 g

VOLUME

US	Metric
1/4 tsp	1 ml
1/2 tsp	2 ml
1 tsp	5 ml
1 tbs	15 ml
1/4 cup (4 tbs)	60 ml
1/3 cup	80 ml
1/2 cup	120 ml
2/3 cup	160 ml
3/4 cup	180 ml
1 cup	240 ml
2 cups	480 ml
4 cups (1 qt)	950 ml

TEMPERATURE

Fahrenheit	Celsius
300	150
325	165
350	175
375	190
400	205
425	220
450	230
475	245

Your Grocery List:

Meat (all the leanest, hormone-free cuts available)
___ 7% lean ground sirloin
___ chicken breasts
___ no-salt, water packed, tuna
___ sliced turkey breast (from the deli)
___ salmon fillets
___ fresh fish

Eggs (free-range, organic)
___ whole chicken eggs
___ egg whites

Dairy (from hormone-free animals)
___ nonfat plain yogurt
___ low fat sour cream
___ low fat mozzarella cheese
___ string cheese
___ low fat cheese
___ low fat cottage cheese
___ heavy whipping cream
___ real butter (unsalted)

Vegetables (organically grown)
___ lettuce
___ cucumber
___ green onion
___ radishes
___ tomatoes
___ mushrooms
___ celery
___ peppers (all varieties)
___ broccoli

(vegetables cont.)
___ cauliflower
___ zucchini
___ cabbage
___ spinach
___ carrots
___ peeled baby carrots
___ cilantro
___ escarole
___ butternut squash
___ acorn squash
___ yams
___ sweet potatoes

Fresh Fruit (organically grown)
___ apples
___ avocados
___ bananas
___ blueberries
___ strawberries
___ cantaloupe
___ grapes
___ grapefruit
___ peaches
___ pineapple
___ papaya
___ plums
___ honeydew
___ mango
___ oranges
___ tangerines
___ watermelon

Raw Nuts (organic and out of the shell)
___ almonds
___ filberts
___ pecans
___ walnuts
___ macadamia
___ flax seeds

Fats and Oils
___ flax seed oil
___ extra virgin olive oil

Grains (organically grown)
___ brown rice
___ millet
___ puffed rice cereal
___ popcorn

Breads and Pasta (from organically grown grains)
___ 100% flourless, sprouted, no salt bread
___ corn tortillas
___ frozen waffles (gluten, wheat, dairy and egg free)
___ corn pastas
___ rice pastas

Specialty Food Items and Supplements
___ whey protein
___ egg white protein
___ soy protein
___ tofu
___ sparkling water
___ stevia liquid (may need to order by mail)
___ Agave (may need to order by mail)
___ baked tortilla chips

Condiments, Herbs and Spices

___ no salt mustard
___ no salt, low fat pasta sauce
___ Braggs Liquid Aminos
___ Knox, unflavored gelatin
___ Red Zinger herb tea
___ herb teas
___ Rosemary flakes
___ nutmeg
___ cinnamon
___ black pepper
___ potassium based salt substitute
___ cayenne pepper
___ basil flakes
___ oregano flakes
___ fresh basil

Quick Reference Guide to Find the Recipes

Other Books and Videos by Jay Robb

BOOKS

The Fat Burning Diet - The original book that started the low-carb diet revolution that has taken the country by storm! Learn the Glycogen Loading Principle that makes The Fat Burning Diet the only low-carb—high-carb diet book on the market that gives you the best of both worlds. Burn fat 24 hours a day, never feel hungry, gain energy, and lose unwanted fat like never before. 224 pages of fun, easy-to-understand information, loaded with menus, recipes and illustrations that can turn your body into a fat burning furnace! $12.95 plus $5 S/H US Funds.

Ultimate Abdominals In 30 Days - This classic book reveals a foolproof program that will get you a washboard stomach, free of fat—and all in 30 days! The exercise routine requires only 7-10 minutes, 3 days per week! This highly effective program contains the ultimate abdominal exercises *and* a special 30 day *fat burning diet plan* that will melt fat like a stick of butter in a hot skillet! This is the *world's only* abdominal program that combines diet and exercise to make your abdominal dreams become a reality! $4.95 plus $5 S/H US Funds

Secrets To Successful Bodybuilding Without Steroids - This classic book teaches you how to get into the shape of your life! Loaded with little-known secrets that will turn your average body into a champion physique! Complete with training programs, diet plans, and every detail you need to succeed! $19.95 plus $5 S/H US Funds

VIDEO

The Fat Burning Diet Seminar - This video is like having Jay Robb right in your living room as he delivers his powerful *Fat Burning Diet Seminar* to you! The perfect accompaniment to Jay's best selling book, *The Fat Burning Diet!* $19.95 plus $5 S/H US Funds

Prices subject to change without notice. For more information on any of the above material, seminars, fitness clubs and/or new releases by Jay Robb please call:

1-877-JAY ROBB • jayrobb.com

Receive a FREE Catalog and Get Monthly Updates on New Books and Products by Jay Robb

Don't miss out on the latest from Jay Robb that can burn fat, get you fit and keep you healthy!

Three ways to get on our mailing list. Please send your name, address, phone and e-mail address to one of the following:

1. e-mail us at: info@jayrobb.com
2. FAX us your information at (760) 634-5490
3. Mail the information to:

Jay Robb Enterprises, Inc.
1530 Encinitas Blvd.
Encinitas, CA 92024

4. Call us toll-free at: 1-877 JAY ROBB
5. Log onto: jayrobb.com and e-mail us there.

In the San Diego area, stop in...

Rapid Fat Loss Is Our Specialty

1474 Encinitas Blvd.
Encinitas, CA 92024

- *Home to Jay Robb's Fat Burning Diet and Fat Burning Diet Workout.*

- *Meet people and make great new friends that have a genuine interest in health and fitness.*

- *Get fit in one hour a week on Jay Robb's 30 Minute Workout.*

- *Nutrition Center featuring Jay Robb's Protein Powders and Complete Supplement Line.*

See us online at: jayrobb.com

or call (760) 634-5494

Open a Jay's Gym in your area!
Franchise Inquiries Welcome!

What Others are Saying About The Fat Burning Diet...

Hello Jay,
"I bought your book based on a positive review I read in Ironman Magazine. I figured that Ironman is very reputable and would not recommend something if it was not what it purported to be. I read your book and it made so much sense. I immediately started on your recommendations and within days felt better. Before I started on your diet I was taking 4-8 prepulsid, for motility problems, per day as well I still needed great quantities of antacids - a large bottle every month. Within days I stopped taking the prepulsid and have only needed antacid tablets once, due to some extra spicy food. It has been six months and I have not felt better in years.

Thank you - Thank you - Thank you. After so many years of abuse my body is slowly changing and I have lost body fat and my weight lifting poundages continue to climb. I share my story with anyone who will listen. You have truly changed my life.

B. S., Nepean, Ontario, Canada

Hi Jay,
I just wanted to say thanks again for the help and guidance your books have provided. Following your Fat Burning Diet, I was able to win the ABA Forever Natural Universe this past May 20th in Las Vegas and also earned my Pro card in the process. This was the first time I had competed since 1987, and at 38 was in better shape than when I was 25. I had previously followed the high carb, low fat method and was always tired and dragged out, but felt great on your diet.
P.S. I noticed that you are franchising your gym? Would it be

*possible to get some more information from you on this? I am
interested in opening my own fitness center in Colorado at
some point soon.*

Thanks.
Todd D., Longmont, CO 80502-2239

Dear Jay,
*I have been on your diet for less than one week - the biggest
bonus has been finally realizing what has been wrong with me.
I was a vegetarian (although I did eat fish occasionally). I was
living in a mental fog with very little energy. It was sometimes
difficult to even complete small tasks - and I run my own small
business. It has been rough!*

*I could not understand it - I was eating the squash, fruits,
vegetables, steel cut oats, minerals, vitamins, - maintained a
fairly low stressful life-style. According to the latest research, I
should have been overflowing with energy.*

*Thanks a bunch - I feel like an entirely new person. I even
sleep much better. I really appreciate the fact that you too went
through similar circumstances and were kind enough to let the
rest of us know how to fine tune ourselves.*

By the way, your Whey Protein is excellent!

Best regards, Nancy

Hi Jay,
*I hope all is doing well in San Diego! This correspondence is
way over due and is a story for your record book. Please feel*

free to share it with others.

We spoke by phone in the early 1990's. I had been flipping through a health magazine and ran across a question/answer article you had published. Little did I know that you were about to, not just change my life, but save my life. As a premature twin, I have suffered severe glucose intolerance difficulties my whole life. The effects were more difficult to manage as I aged. With frequent blood sugar readings between 37-55, I was lost in a world of "I am sorry I don't know how to help you." It was unbearable at times.

When I shared this with you I remember you saying, "I never thought I would meet the person I wrote my book for." Most were interested in weight control vs. insulin control. Well, I am happy to share with you that within 5-7 days of your guidance with dietary changes my system began to regulate. Only you know the realities of what this condition truly brings to one's life.

Over the years I have purchased many copies of your book to share with others. I will confess I even sent one to Oprah Winfrey. I love the second edition by the way! I knew you had found something special. I became so much better in fact, I have owned and operated a Wellness Center the last seven years. This would not have been attainable without gaining proper health and strength through glucose management. Thanks for sharing what you had found with the rest of us.

Jay, I send a lifetime of thanks and appreciation for helping me. I know your record book must be huge but please squeeze mine in!

Smiles Always,
Candace B.

Dear Jay,
WOW! What a difference!
I cannot tell you how much better I feel since being on "The Fat Burning Diet". It's been about five weeks now, and I feel better each day. I have tremendous energy, and I can actually feel my body getting stronger.

I happened to see you on KUSI Channel 9 in San Diego one Sunday morning when you introduced Chocolate Pudding. Well, I love chocolate pudding, so I inquired further on the web to get your wonderful recipe and to find out more. Needless to say, I ordered the book, Whey Protein and Agave. This was the beginning of a wonderful new life.

In March of 2000, I learned I had severe Thyroid Disease. It wasn't until I read your book that I realized that my so called, healthy diet (complex carbs, low protein, low fat) caused my disease and ALMOST KILLED ME! I have always tried to take care of myself by eating right (I thought) and exercising.

If I would have not forced myself to got to work each day, do mild exercises and take vitamin supplements, I probably would not be writing to you today. Prior to being diagnosed, I cannot express to you how sick and depressed I felt. I never conveyed to anyone, other than my doctors, how I felt, as I did not want to give POWER to the disorder.

God created perfection, and we really messed things up along the way. THANK YOU SO MUCH FOR SHARING YOUR WONDERFUL GIFT!! My warmest personal regards to you, your family and ALL who support your efforts.

Dolores J., San Diego, CA

Dear Jay,

Thank you, thank you, a million times over for writing "The Fat Burning Diet"! I cannot tell you just how much this diet has changed my life

To begin with, I was trying for years (with much frustration) to get leaner. I would do at least 60 minutes of aerobics 6 days a week with no results. I also had trouble gaining muscle. I was following a high-carb diet which contained about 73% carbohydrate, 12% protein and 10% or less of fat.

While following this diet regime I was experiencing severe hypoglycemia and felt like I was in bondage to food because I couldn't live a normal life. I had to eat something every hour at times and that was difficult when you travel or go anywhere. I suffered with dizziness, headaches, confusion, mental fog, panic, mood swings, energy dips, and major intestinal problems probably associated with Candida (yeast overgrowth).

I've been on The Fat Burning Diet for about six months now, and the difference is like day and night! No more hypoglycemia! I don't really ever feel hungry, my energy level is stable and I need a lot less sleep. My bodyfat is down from 20% to around 13% and I'm finally able to put on muscle. My intestinal problems are gone and I feel so incredible now that it seems too good to be true.

I feel like I'm on top of the world!
Thanks again!

Kim C., San Clemente, CA

Dear Jay,

I am a top-ranking bodybuilder holding the title of NABBA Mr. USA 1994. In 1993 I suffered an injury that landed me in the hospital, confined to bed, for SIX WEEKS. Ironically, upon my release from the hospital, I ended up weighing only 1 pound more than the day I was first injured and hospitalized. This amazing feat was done by controlling my carbs (like you outline in your book, "The Fat Burning Diet").

And the beauty of my weight controlling accomplishment is the fact that I never had to count a calorie, plus I ate eggs, bacon, and one pound of red meat EVERYDAY! I also continued to take in several ounces of Egg White Protein each day also.

There is no doubt this way of eating helped speed my healing and recovery. I'm 34 years old, and when I got into bodybuilding in 1975, everyone did the high-protein, low-low carb diet. I personally get weak, small and tired on high-carb diets.

Thank you for writing your book and for such a great line of low-carb protein powders!

Your friend,
Buddy D., Hicksville, NY

Dear Jay

After years of searching for a diet that would supply me with stable energy throughout the day, I finally found yours and my life has changed dramatically. I don't suffer from energy slumps anymore and can wait for meal times without depending on snacks. Also, my weight has stabilized and I think I am now at my ideal weight. My wife is doing great. She has been able to easily melt-away those difficult areas of fat that had deposited on her body.

Thank you very, very much,
S. E., Rancho Santa Fe, CA

Dear Jay,
"From the time I began reading your book, I was captivated. I was consuming too many carbohydrates and I suffered every symptom associated with high-carb intake such as fatigue, mental confusion, lack of energy, and high bodyfat levels.

After discovering your diet, I changed immediately to your plan and by the fourth day I was feeling incredible. When I began your diet my bodyfat was at 18%. After eight weeks my bodyfat levels dropped to 15% and my strength was skyrocketing.

The conventional high-carbohydrate, moderate protein, low-fat diet was getting me nowhere. To me, this book was a Godsend. I am a personal trainer and recommend this book to all my clients and anyone who suffers from the symptoms of high carbohydrate eating.

Your book has been written in such a way that everyone would enjoy reading it and benefit from its message. I would just like to take the opportunity to say thank you. Your book has made a big difference in my life.

I have been referring people to you for a copy of your book. Sometime in the near future I would like to discuss the possibility of carrying some of your products at my training facility."

Thanks again for everything,
Dan R., Batavia, IL

Dear Jay,
Thank you for your book, The Fat Burning Diet. It has added another dimension to my knowledge on fine tuning my diet.

I think you might remember Reo H. Blair and Vince Gironda who both had their versions of the high-protein diet. I like your book because it offers a very balanced approach. I believe this style of eating is very beneficial, especially to athletes who workout without the aid of steroids or injectable growth hormone.

I think once athletes use the "drugs" it kind of makes everything idiot proof. The drugs actually enhance the metabolism of carbs and I believe the high-carb diet came into vogue at the same time as steroid abuse. But once the athlete discontinues the use of the "juice", and yet keeps following the high-carb, low-fat diet, he or she automatically becomes fat and out of shape. And, this sudden weight/fat gain drives them back to use the drugs again so they can get the same results as before.

Prohibition has never worked because steroids are more prevalent than ever. I think education is what's needed and your eating approach certainly is a big step in the right direction.

More power to you and please keep me on you mailing list for any new books and products you produce in the future.

Best wishes,
John Terilli, Pro Mr. Universe
Sydney, Australia

Dear Jay,

"I bought your book and I have never been happier with my body than now, thanks to your diet. My son, who is 26, and I work out together and your book has been great for both of us.

I am 51 years old and because of your diet my body has never been in such great shape. (Plus I look 20 years younger!) It all comes down to eliminating the carbs I thought I had to eat.

I wish I could attend one of your fat burning seminars. I am 5'3" and weight a perfect 108 lb. now. And since I have been following your great diet, my stomach is flat and my workouts are getting me excellent results.

You are wonderful and we both thank you again."

Sincerely
Joie L., New Orleans, LA

*Tell Us YOUR Success Story and Help Inspire Others!

Yes, we want to hear from you and your triumph with weight loss, energy gain, fitness, fat burning, and transforming your body while following "The Fat Burning Diet", and using the recipes outlined in "The Fat Burning Diet COK BOOK".

Your story can serve to inspire millions of individuals to break their addiction to carbohydrates and regain control of their life.

*Share Your Favorite Recipe With Me...

I am always looking for new fat burning recipes, so if you have a favorite one, please share it with me. If I publish your recipe in my next book, I will be sure and give your credit!

Don't be shy. Write out your story and/or recipe and...

1. e-mail it to: info@jayrobb.com
2. fax it to: (760) 634-5490
3. mail it to:

> Jay Robb Enterprises, Inc.
> 1530 Encinitas Blvd.
> Encinitas, CA 92024

Thank you for reading my Cook Book. I hope you have had as much fun reading it as I have writing it..

Your comments and suggestions are always welcome.

Please be aware that, due to the volume of mail we receive daily, we won't be able to answer each letter or return anything submitted.

Success is Sweet

With hopes on high
You give up the pie
And other taste treats
Including whole wheat

You struggle at first
Expecting the worst
But after two days
You lift from the haze

Your thoughts become clear
Without any fear
As the fat melts away
Day after day

Then suddenly you see
You truly are free
From the bondage of food
Controlling your mood

And your Life opens wide
With nothing to hide
You are now free to do
Whatever you choose

As you travel by feel
On this big turning wheel
For success is now real
Meal after meal

It isn't a front
You get what you want
For success, health and zeal
Are in the cards that *you* deal